The Open University

T357
Structural integrity:
designing against failure

BLOCK 1
STRESS ANALYSIS

PART 5: STRUCTURAL ANALYSIS

This publication forms part of an Open University course T357 *Structural integrity: designing against failure*. Details of this and other Open University courses can be obtained from the Student Registration and Enquiry Service, The Open University, PO Box 197, Milton Keynes MK7 6BJ, United Kingdom: tel. +44 (0)845 300 60 90, email general-enquiries@open.ac.uk

Alternatively, you may visit the Open University website at http://www.open.ac.uk where you can learn more about the wide range of courses and packs offered at all levels by The Open University.

To purchase a selection of Open University course materials visit http://www.ouw.co.uk, or contact Open University Worldwide, Walton Hall, Milton Keynes MK7 6AA, United Kingdom for a brochure. tel. +44 (0)1908 858793; fax +44 (0)1908 858787; email ouw-customer-services@open.ac.uk

The Open University
Walton Hall, Milton Keynes
MK7 6AA

First published 2007. Second edition 2009.

Edited and designed by The Open University.

Typeset by SR Nova Pvt. Ltd, Bangalore, India.

Printed in the United Kingdom by Latimer Trend and Company Ltd, Plymouth.

ISBN 978 0 7492 5263 2

2.1

FSC
www.fsc.org
MIX
Paper from responsible sources
FSC® C013436

The paper used in this publication contains pulp sourced from forests independently certified to the Forest Stewardship Council (FSC) principles and criteria. Chain of custody certification allows the pulp from these forests to be tracked to the end use (see www.fsc.org).

PART 5
STRUCTURAL ANALYSIS

CONTENTS

1 INTRODUCTION

So far in this course we have concentrated on the structural integrity of individual components, and have not worried about the other parts of the structure or machine to which they are connected. We have shown how we can use *stress analysis* to predict the distribution of stress and strain in a component provided we know both the geometry of the component and all the forces acting on it. Armed with this knowledge we can then, for example, predict whether the stress in any part of the component exceeds a certain critical value, such as the yield strength of the material, which could result in extensive deformation or breakage.

To perform stress analysis, we need to know the magnitude and direction of all the loads acting on a component. This may be quite straightforward in some cases. Let's take the example of a tower crane, such as that shown in Figure 5.1; this is a common sight in most cities, with typically over a thousand being used at any one time in the UK alone. Analysing some parts of the crane structure is straightforward: the crane hook must be subjected to a force of magnitude equal to the weight of the load the crane carries, for example. However, the forces on many other members of the crane structure are more difficult to calculate. The load that is created by the weight of the hook and its attached cargo in Figure 5.1 is transferred to the ground through the cable attached to the hook, and through the jib (or arm) and mast. The jib and mast are constructed as a steel framework (i.e. a network of jointed structural members, known as a *braced structure*) and calculation of the loads on one individual member of the structure requires the application of the principle of equilibrium to all of the members, as well as to the whole structure.

It is, of course, important to know these loads, since that will allow the design of the crane to be optimized. Knowing the loads helps to ensure the crane will not fail, or to trace the cause if a failure does occur. Unfortunately, the collapse of cranes due to

Figure 5.1   A tower crane in use

Figure 5.2   Collapse of a tower crane

structural failure is not unknown. When a crane does fail catastrophically, as in the case shown in Figure 5.2, then the failure usually occurs in a single component – the weakest link in the structure – and it is clearly vital to be able to calculate what the loads are at these locations. In the case shown in Figure 5.2, high winds caused the crane's jib to bend and collapse, crushing the operator's cab in the process. Luckily, the accident happened on a Sunday morning when the site was unoccupied, and so no one was injured. The reason for the collapse in this case was not clear, but it was believed to be related to the failure (mechanical or otherwise) of the release for the 'slew brake', which normally allows the jib to rotate away from the wind so that it doesn't catch its full force.

The process of calculating the loads in the component members of a structure from the geometry and loads applied *to the structure* is known as *structural analysis*, the topic of this part. Stress and structural analyses are complementary branches of engineering design and analysis. The process of designing a structure or artefact can be broadly broken down into the following decisions or actions:

- selection of the form (geometry) and materials to be used for the structure

- determination or conservative estimation of the external loads that can be expected to act on the structure

- calculation of the stresses and deformations that are produced in the individual components of the structure by the external loads, as well as by its own self-load (weight)

- calculation of the size and geometry of the individual components to avoid exceeding known limits of behaviour (e.g. yielding or buckling).

Figure 5.3   Leonardo da Vinci's painting, the *Mona Lisa*

Of course, these decisions interact with each other and so are usually approached iteratively. Furthermore, cost, aesthetics, and materials or component availability can also influence the final design. But these basic elements of structural and stress analysis are present in some form in everything we make, whether it is a bridge, a building, a ship, or even a work of art. When Leonardo da Vinci produced his famous painting the *Mona Lisa* (Figure 5.3) he would have decided on the type of wood and the size of the frame in the same way as the paint he used. Furthermore, if any of these decisions had been wrong the structure of the painting might not have remained stable over the centuries and the lady's smile might have been even more enigmatic!

In fact there's an important point here. Although I can't be sure, especially with a genius like Leonardo, I suspect that he did not need to perform any calculations to decide how thick to make his board (Leonardo painted the *Mona Lisa* on poplar wood), or how big to make his frame. He most probably used what had worked before, i.e. he drew on previous experience, which is sometimes termed *heuristic knowledge*. Such knowledge is crucial, since there are very few occasions when the results of our stress and structural analyses are exact. Whenever we use mathematical calculations, however sophisticated, concerning a real structure we have to make some assumptions about its behaviour and the environment in which it will operate. To ensure structural integrity, then, we need to make sure that the structures we formulate are conservative, i.e. that they are designed to take larger loads than they will see in service. The common ways of ensuring this are described in ▽ **Ensuring conservatism in engineering design** ▽.

☑ Ensuring conservatism in engineering design

Factors of safety

The earliest (and still quite widespread) approach to allowing for uncertainty in engineering design calculations is to add a safety factor to the predicted performance required in the material. Effectively, this reduces the actual values for material properties entered into the calculations to allow for variability in true performance. Safety factor values between 1.2 and 2.5 are typical, depending on the material and the need to ensure absolute safety. As understanding of materials and control over their formulation and processing have improved, safety factors have tended to be reduced. If the failure strength of a material is known to within ±30 MPa rather than ±100 MPa, then a design using the material can be less conservative.

Load factors

A more recent approach concentrates not on potential variability in the materials but on the loads applied to the structure. Thus, load factors are applied to the predicted working loads in design calculations to create a safety margin for performance.

For either of these two approaches, i.e. factors of safety and load factors, high factors need to be applied to provide confidence in the safety of a structure. This is because each ignores the contribution to the variability in performance accounted for by the other. So, how can we safely avoid the tendency to overdesign? The answer is to use a more sophisticated approach, combining the probabilities of circumstances arising that are outside the norm. This is called *limit-state design*.

Limit-state design

Limit-state design allows the application of a *partial factor* γ to both the applied loads, γ_f, and the materials data (strength, modulus, etc.), γ_m. The partial factors are adjusted for combinations of types of loading and for particular limit states. Thus, the probability of overloading in one way may be compensated for by underloading in another. Design calculations for an 'ultimate' limit state (safety-critical parameters such as yielding or fracture) use higher partial factors than those for 'serviceability' limit states (such things as vibration or corrosion).

As an example, if the load on a component is simply that arising from the weight of the structure, then that load is subject to a partial factor of 1.4 when designing against collapse. Loads such as snow on a roof or the weight of a roofing contractor doing repairs attract a partial factor of 1.6. Wind loads are treated differently and subjected to a partial factor of 1.4 when they might contribute to the structure overturning or toppling. The design load ▷

resulting from a combination of any two of these loadings is obtained from a straightforward application of the relevant partial factors. For a live load and a self-load, therefore:

design load = (1.6 × live load) + (1.4 × self-load)

If all three appear in the calculations, they are reduced to 1.2 to allow for the cumulative probability effect mentioned above. That gives:

design load = 1.2 × (self-load + live load + wind load)

Similarly, the partial factor for materials performance γ_m takes different values for different materials. Thus, structural steel has $\gamma_m = 1.0$, implying total confidence in the published values of strength. On the other hand, reinforced concrete, a notoriously unpredictable material, attracts a partial factor of 1.5 for the concrete and 1.15 for the reinforcement in ultimate limit-state design, introducing an allowance for the variability in the standards of manufacture. Notice that the partial factors for material strength are greater than or equal to one, just as in loading, but this means that the material-strength data must be *divided* by the partial factor in design calculations in order to provide a safety margin.

Characteristic strength, characteristic load

Finally, one further allowance is made for statistical variability in data for design calculations. The two categories of data, materials properties and loads, are treated in this regard in two quite different ways.

If we make repeated measurements of a materials property we usually get a distribution of values clustered around the mean or average value. I mentioned above the use of average figures for materials properties. We will not explore the statistical theory here, but there is an assumption that where we have a large number of test results for a particular property, say tensile strength, they will follow a typical normal distribution, as seen in Figure 5.4.

The spread of the results is described by the standard deviation SD. Knowing the standard deviation allows us to predict the likelihood of the strength of the material in a real product falling above or below a certain value relative to the average or mean.

Applying these ideas, limit-state design requires the use of the *characteristic strength* of a material, that being the value of strength below which not more than 1 in 20 (i.e. 5%) of the test results for that property would be expected to fail. The mathematics of normal distributions give this as:

characteristic strength = mean strength − 1.64 SD

So the properties of a material used for design calculations are downrated still further by a factor that increases with the degree of variability in the measurements of those properties.

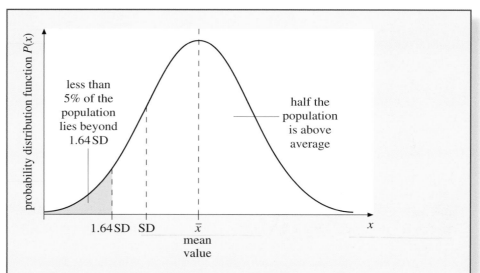

Figure 5.4 A normal distribution curve based on the probability of occurrence can help with engineering predictions

It would be attractive if this approach could be applied to loads as well as to materials, but the characterizing of loads in terms of a normal distribution of values makes no sense. The uncertainty in a load is not necessarily governed by statistics. Nevertheless, some account also has to be made of variability in loads. Limit-state design, therefore, defines a characteristic load. However, this is arrived at by a consensus of expert views rather than by mathematical theory.

One vital point to remember about limit-state design is that the partial factors assigned to design parameters for given limit states are arrived at by a combination of science and judgement (heuristic knowledge again). They are 'empirical' values based on experience, that have been found to give an adequate balance between reliability and cost. It would be wrong, though, to think that they correspond to specific loading conditions.

The degree of conservatism we use in any structural design is, of course, also influenced by other constraints on the design, such as cost, weight or size. Indeed, as noted in ▽ **The cost of structural integrity** ▽, it is possible to argue that all decisions are actually based on cost. What is important to remember is that, by making assumptions about a structure, we can develop mathematical models to predict the forces, stresses and deformations that will be produced in the structure and hence can perform calculations that predict its structural integrity. In critically important cases, or where a large degree of conservatism is not desirable, these predictions are then validated by experiments. A classic example of this approach is in commercial aircraft structures. Here weight is paramount, so the very sophisticated design calculations are verified by full-scale testing of critical structures to destruction, as shown in Figure 5.5.

Figure 5.5　Full-scale test of the Airbus A380 wing

▽ The cost of structural integrity

There are a number of definitions of engineering or, to be more precise, definitions of mechanical/materials engineering that centre around statements of the type:

> The design and manufacture of machines, structures and systems that fulfil their expected missions and ensure structural integrity throughout their operational life while minimizing cost.

Your first thought on reading this definition might be: 'Cost to whom?' There is at least one family car currently on sale in the UK where it is recommended that the car is returned to an approved service agent to change the headlamp bulb. I suspect that no one costed the owner's time in that design decision … But an important consequence of this definition is the question 'What is the cost of structural integrity?'. We can always reduce the probability of failure of a given engineering system by spending more money on design and manufacture, even though anything we design can never be 100% safe. In practice, of course, it all depends on the situation and context. If we designed and operated all technology on the basis that human life is priceless, then modern civilization would grind to a halt. How safe is 'safe enough' is a recurring question that practising engineers answer, either explicitly or implicitly, on a daily basis. ▷

In some areas, particularly where the state is the investor, actual monetary costs are put on a human life to help decision making. For example, the notional cost of saving a human life by making a traffic or road improvement in the UK is currently of the order of £1–10 million. But even when an explicit monetary cost is not used, all engineering is undertaken under financial constraints, and any decision to improve the structural integrity of a design will be taken only if the cost is appropriate to the benefit that will be achieved. These decisions will also become increasingly important as both materials and energy become less abundant in an ever-developing world economy.

2 STRUCTURES

2.1 What is a structure?

Now, before going any further, let me explain what I mean by *engineering structure*, or simply *structure*, in the context of this course. A structure may be defined as a member, or assembly of members, intended to support loads. Within such an assembly the load is transmitted from one place to another by the structure. For a crane, the load is ultimately supported by the ground on which the crane is erected or parked, and the structure of a crane supports the load by transmitting it to the ground. In a similar way, a bridge supports the vehicles on it by transmitting their weight to the ground on either side of the river, valley or whatever. The members of a structure can have all sorts of sizes and shapes and can be made from many different materials. This includes not only bridges and buildings as structures, but also aeroplanes and ships, chairs and bookcases, and casings of mobile phones and laptops.

'Supporting the load' does not sound specific enough to describe a structure. I should really add that while performing its intended function, the structure must not collapse, and it must not deform extensively either. Indeed, a structure as a whole, and each individual member, must be designed with reference to the three S's: strength, stiffness and stability:

- The *strength* of a structure is the ability to carry the applied loads without yielding or breaking.

- *Stiffness* is the ability to carry the applied loads without too much distortion or movement. As you are now well aware, a material can sustain stress only at the expense of some strain ($\sigma = E\varepsilon$). Sometimes the strain, or deflection, may be the limiting factor.

- The *stability* of a structure is the ability to carry compressive loads without collapsing or buckling out of shape. For example, a long metal rod in compression longitudinally can bow out of shape (buckle) under a compressive load well below that which would cause compressive yield.

So how exactly do we go about analysing a structure to find the forces and changes in shape (deformations) under loading? Moreover, how can we design a new structure, e.g. a bridge, and be confident that it will not collapse? As noted earlier, by making assumptions about a structure we can develop models to predict the forces, stresses and deformations that are produced within it. Of course, the complexity of these calculations depends on how many simplifying assumptions we can make.

One approach would be to perform a relatively simple calculation, knowing that it may be fairly inaccurate, and then to include in our design a high degree of conservatism using the techniques described in 'Ensuring conservatism in engineering design'. Alternatively, we could use a far more sophisticated model, perhaps employing large, complex, finite element descriptions of our structure, in order to obtain a more accurate prediction of the in-service stresses and deflections. The important thing to remember is that all structural and stress analyses are models of reality. They may differ in their realism and potential accuracy, but none is a perfect description; thus, an element of conservatism must be included in all structural design.

I will describe only relatively simple models of structural analysis in this course, but knowledge of these approaches is critical to understanding even the most modern structural analysis methods, since:

- they illustrate the fundamental principles of structural analysis

- they enable relatively quick, 'back of the envelope' checks to be made of more complex, less accessible analyses

- they enable the user to *converse* with practitioners of more complex analysis procedures (such as the ubiquitous finite element method)

- they can estimate the size and geometry needed for individual components to avoid exceeding known limits of behaviour (e.g. yielding or buckling).

This means that the general principles of structural analysis may be understood by studying the design of simple structures. In this course we shall concentrate on two-dimensional analysis. This is not a serious restriction, as you can learn the principles of structural analysis without becoming involved in the extra complication of three dimensions. As you will see, there are many engineering structures that can be analysed using a two-dimensional approach.

2.2 Idealization of structural forms

Much of the skill of engineering lies in being able to make the right simplifications to complex problems. In the present context, the resulting idealized structure should be a sufficiently accurate representation of the real structure and should also be as easy as possible to analyse. A good way of simplifying structures is to classify their members into a small number of structural forms. The simplest way of dividing up all the possible structural forms is by the main types of stress that develop when the structure is resisting applied load. The main structural types are as follows.

Cables

The easiest way of transmitting a load between two points is to use a cable, as shown in Figure 5.6(a). Here the load is in equilibrium with the tension in the cable. Since the load must be balanced by a vertical load in the cable the cable must sag, and the greater the sag the lower is the tension required in the cable.

EXERCISE 5.1

You can show that the greater the sag, the lower is the tension required in the cable. Do this by working out the tension in the cable in Figure 5.6(a) in terms of the weight W for the conditions where the cable makes angles of 45°, 60° and 75° to the vertical. Assume that the weight of the cable is negligible, and that the load is applied at the centre of the cable.

Hint: if you cannot remember how to produce the free-body diagram (FBD) and resolve the identified forces to prove this, read the input ☑ **Equilibrium of forces** ☑ *and its companion* ☑ **Equilibrium of moments** ☑, *which follow this section.*

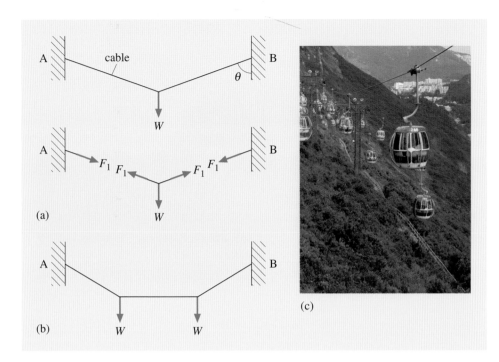

Figure 5.6   Cable with (a) a single point load and (b) two point loads (note that I have used W to indicate a weight load acting at a point); (c) Hong Kong cable cars

If there are several loads on the cable, then it changes its shape as shown in Figure 5.6(b), and this ability is used to the full in multiple-car aerial tramways, such as that shown in Figure 5.6(c). Cables are the easiest members to analyse in any structure, as their flexibility means that they can sustain a tensile load but not compression or bending stresses. The shape a cable takes under load is known as its *funicular curve*. If the loading is uniform along the horizontal length of the rope, then the cable will adopt a parabolic shape: the main suspension cables of a suspension bridge have an approximately parabolic funicular curve, as illustrated by the original Severn road crossing shown in Figure 5.7.

Figure 5.7   The Severn suspension bridge

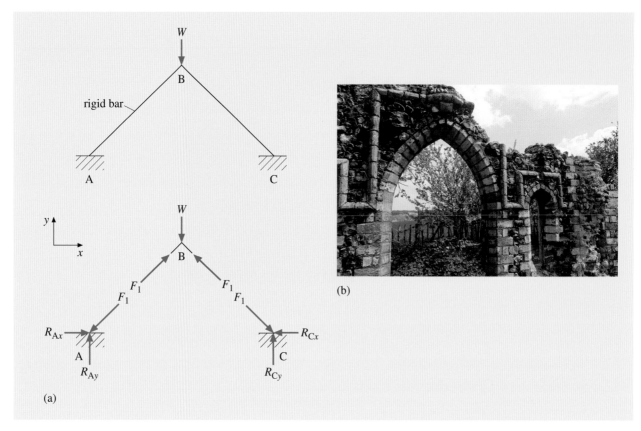

Figure 5.8 (a) Simple arch (note that I have used R to denote a reaction force); (b) a Gothic arch

Arches

If we just invert Figure 5.6(a) and replace the cables with rigid bars we get a simple arch, as shown in Figure 5.8. Arches are designed so that their shape results in the predominant loading producing a uniform compressive stress in the arch. Indeed, the main loading of large masonry bridges is often their self-weight and under these conditions, as for cables, the optimum arch shape is parabolic. However, unlike a cable, because an arch cannot change its shape, bending stresses are produced for some loading conditions.

Trusses

We will look at truss structures in more detail later in this part, since the assumption that the members in a truss can only be subjected to axial loads (tension or compression) will allow us to create the simplest models possible in structural analysis.

The lower ends of the simple arch shown in Figure 5.8 must create horizontal and vertical reaction forces (R_x and R_y respectively) at points A and C. If we connect A and C with a third bar, or even a cable (since this member must be in tension), then we create a truss. The general definition of a truss is a stable system of axially stressed members, where some are in tension and some are in compression, arranged in the form of one or more triangles.

If we take the three-member truss shown in Figure 5.9(a) and load it from point D, halfway between A and C (Figure 5.9b), rather than at point B, then the structure no longer behaves like a truss. The load is now transmitted to the supports not by axial stresses in the bars, but by bending of the member AC. So the member AC becomes a beam, which we will consider next, and the members AB and BC become redundant. To make the system a truss again we can add another member BD (Figure 5.9c), which will be loaded in tension and will transmit load down to the supports by compressive stresses in AB and BC. As may be seen from Figure 5.9(d), trusses are commonly used in both bridge and roof structures.

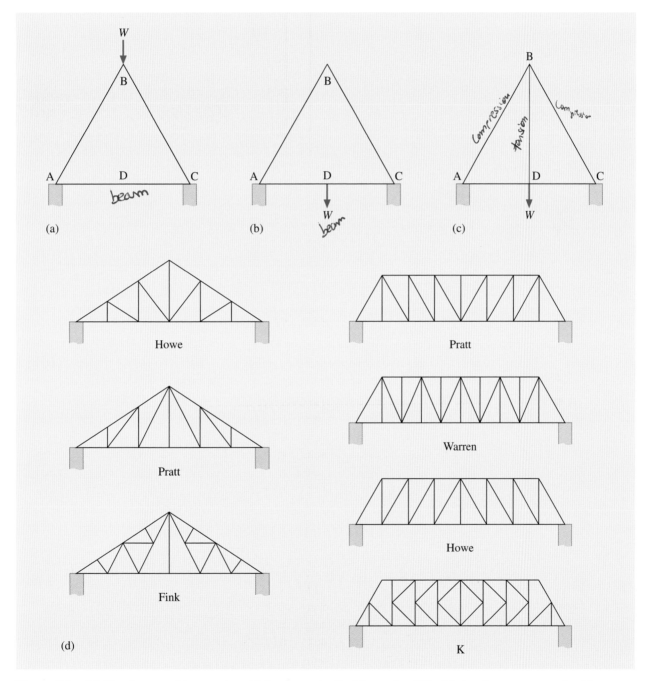

Figure 5.9   (a) Simple truss; (b) structure with load at point D; (c) member BD added to form a truss again; (d) some truss structures commonly used in roof supports and bridges (you won't have to remember the names or forms of these trusses: they are just for illustration)

Figure 5.10 (a) Simple beam; (b) bending stresses; (c) similarity between a deep beam and a truss

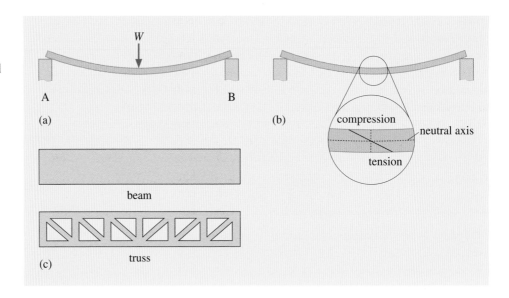

Beams

A beam, such as the simple beam shown in Figure 5.10(a), transfers a vertical force or weight load W laterally to the supports at A and B by <u>bending.</u> The beam becomes curved, causing a <u>compressive stress to be formed on its inner radius</u> and a <u>tensile stress to be formed on its outer radius</u>, as shown in Figure 5.10(b). We will be studying beams and bending in detail in Part 6 of this block. One of the principal advantages of beams is that, unlike cables and arches, they <u>do not produce any horizontal forces at their ends</u>. They can also be quite compact, and so are often used to support floors in buildings and on bridges. One disadvantage is that they do not use material very efficiently. A cable or the axially loaded member of a truss can be uniformly loaded up to the allowable stress for the material. In contrast, <u>a beam can be loaded only to the allowable material stress *on its surface*</u>; the bulk of the beam is loaded to a lower stress and the material at the centre of the beam, at the neutral axis, is not loaded at all (Figure 5.10b).

We will see how to produce more efficient beams later in the course; for now, just note that, as illustrated in Figure 5.10(c), a truss can be produced just by removing material from a beam, which suggests that the truss uses material more efficiently.

Surface elements: membranes, plates and shells

All the above structural elements transfer loads in just one dimension. Surface elements can transfer loads in two orthogonal directions simultaneously. *Membranes* are sheets of material that are loaded in tension and so can be thought of as two-dimensional cables. Balloons, sails, parachutes and the tent shown in Figure 5.11(a) are examples of membrane structures. If we pressurize the inside of a closed membrane structure, as in a balloon or a car tyre, then the structure can resist compressive external loads. The trick is to make sure that the pressure is high enough to ensure that the membrane remains in tension. Loads that would usually produce a compressive stress at the surface then reduce only the tension that is there already.

Plates and shells are surfaces that also have stiffness in their transverse direction and so can withstand bending stresses as well as tensile and compressive stresses. Plates can be thought of as two-dimensional beams, while shells are simply curved plates. As a consequence, shells can resist applied loads through the development of in-plane stresses. This can be seen by comparing Figures 5.11(b) and (c). The applied force or the weight load W can be resisted by the vertical components of the compressive forces developed in the shell, while in the plate the forces that resist the applied load are perpendicular to the plate and are the shear forces that cause bending in the plate. Finally, we can think of a shell as a series of two-dimensional arches, and if the curvature of the shell is in two dimensions then we can envisage double-curved surfaces such as that in the *dome* shown in Figure 5.11(d). Domes can be very efficient structures, and they can be used to cover large spaces, as does the dome of St Paul's Cathedral in London (Figure 5.11e). Domes are often used where structural integrity is paramount, for example in the construction of nuclear-reactor containment vessels (Figure 5.11f).

Of course, these idealizations are useful when deciding how to model real structures, which may be combinations of a number of these basic structural forms. We will now look at examples of a few of these forms in greater detail. Others will be considered later in the course.

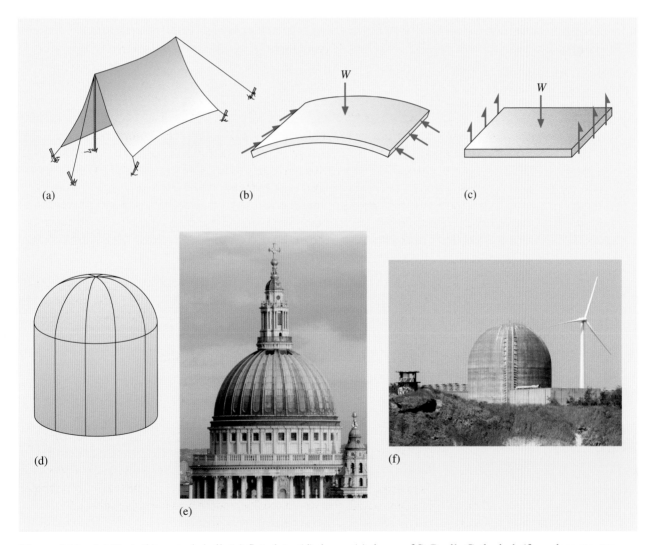

Figure 5.11 (a) Tent; (b) curved shell; (c) flat plate; (d) dome; (e) dome of St Paul's Cathedral; (f) nuclear-reactor containment vessel

☑ Equilibrium of forces

Force is a *vector* quantity, i.e. it has both *magnitude* and *direction*. In addition to its magnitude and direction, structural analysis requires that the line of action and point of application of a force are defined. Forces are usually categorized into *body forces* and *surface* (or *contact*) *forces*. Body forces are caused by the remote action of gravitational, magnetic, or electric forces. The most important body force that you encounter in this course is the *weight* of an object: weight $W = mg$, where m is an object's mass in kg and g is the acceleration due to gravity, equal to 9.81 m s^{-2}. Weight is a force, and has the units of newtons (N).

Surface forces, on the other hand, are generated by direct physical contact between objects: the push or pull, for example, that you apply to an object is categorized as a surface force.

How the external loads give rise to internal forces in members can be explained using Newton's laws. The underlying principle of structural analysis is then to identify and balance the forces and moments acting on the structure and any surroundings with which it interacts. A system of forces is said to be in equilibrium if all the forces and moments acting on the system have a vector sum of zero. I will not, however, use the vector notation and vector algebra in this course to carry out calculations involving forces and moments; it is simpler to deal with *scalar* quantities and their geometries (i.e. directions and angles) in two-dimensional systems. So, the equilibrium of forces and moments in a two-dimensional system, taking the usual xy-coordinate system as the frame of reference, can be described by the mathematical expressions:

$$\sum F_x = 0$$
$$\sum F_y = 0$$
$$\sum M = 0 \qquad (5.1)$$

where F_x is the component of any force in the x-direction, F_y is the component of any force in the y-direction and M_P is the moment of any force

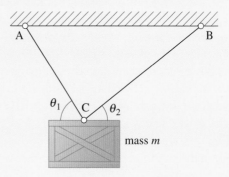

Figure 5.12   Crate of mass m hung from ceiling

about any point P in the xy-plane. In Equation (5.1), the $\sum$ symbol denotes 'the sum of'; i.e. $\sum F_x$ denotes the summation of all the forces acting in the x-direction. The equilibrium of moments is dealt with in 'Equilibrium of moments'.

To illustrate how equilibrium of forces can be used to analyse structures, consider the simple system shown in Figure 5.12, where a crate of mass m is hung from the ceiling by two unequal-length cables attached by an eyebolt on the upper surface of the crate. Let's calculate the magnitude and direction of forces in each cable, AC and BC, if $m = 100$ kg and the angles that the cable makes with the horizontal are $\theta_1 = 60°$ and $\theta_2 = 30°$.

The crate is in static equilibrium (as it is not moving), so all the forces acting on it must sum to zero (Newton's Second Law of Motion). Figure 5.13(a) shows the crate on its own, with arrows representing the forces acting on it. This is called a *free-body diagram* (FBD), a very important concept in analysis of engineering mechanics problems. It helps to define all the forces acting on a *body* and to identify the known and unknown quantities. An FBD can be drawn for all or part of a structure, as long as care is taken to show only the forces acting *on* the body. When drawing an FBD it is not necessary to show internal details of a structure; in fact, an outline of the body would be better, as it clearly defines a boundary between the body and the environment, so that the depiction of forces acting on the body won't be obscured by unnecessary details.

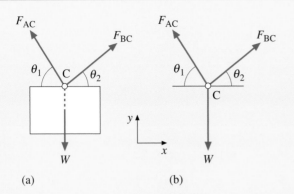

Figure 5.13 (a) Free-body diagram of the crate; (b) free-body diagram of the eyebolt

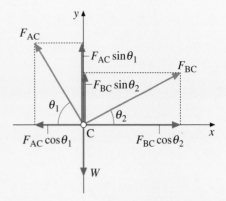

Figure 5.14 The components of the forces acting on the eyebolt

Assuming the eyebolt is in line with the *centre of gravity* of the crate, all the forces in the FBD of Figure 5.13(a) are acting concurrently at the eyebolt. As I am interested only in the forces in the cables AC and BC, I do not need to include the crate in the FBD at all; so, I will consider only the FBD of the eyebolt, shown in Figure 5.13(b).

There are three forces acting on the eyebolt: the weight of the crate W and the unknown forces F_{AC} and F_{BC} exerted by the cables AC and BC respectively. We can find the unknown forces by using the fact that the summation of all the forces acting on the eyebolt must be zero (for *static equilibrium*). To avoid possible confusion with directions, I take the usual xy-coordinate system as my frame of reference. In this part, I will follow the convention that along the vertical y-direction a positive force points upwards, and a negative force acts downwards. Similarly, the forces acting towards the right in the positive x-direction will have a positive sign and forces pointing left will be negative. As the orientations of F_{AC} and F_{BC} do not coincide with the axes of our rectangular coordinate system, we need to resolve the forces into their components along the x- and y-directions. Using trigonometric relations, orthogonal components F_x and F_y are calculated as follows:

$$F_x = F\cos\theta$$

$$F_y = F\sin\theta \text{ or } F_y = F\cos(90 - \theta)$$

In Figure 5.14, I have shown all the forces acting on the object and shown the components of F_{AC} and F_{BC}.

Now, as we have forces acting only in either the x- or the y-direction, we can apply the equilibrium equations given in Equation (5.1). First, the summation of all the forces acting in the x-direction is equal to zero, i.e.:

$$\sum F_x = 0$$
$$F_{ACx} + F_{BCx} = 0$$
$$-F_{AC}\cos\theta_1 + F_{BC}\cos\theta_2 = 0 \tag{5.2}$$

and similarly in the y-direction:

$$\sum F_y = 0$$
$$F_{ACy} + F_{BCy} + W = 0$$
$$F_{AC}\sin\theta_1 + F_{BC}\sin\theta_2 - mg = 0 \tag{5.3}$$

Thus, we have two unknowns (F_{AC} and F_{BC}), and two independent equations, Equations (5.2) and (5.3), that can be solved simultaneously. Rearranging Equation (5.2) gives:

$$F_{AC} = F_{BC}\frac{\cos\theta_2}{\cos\theta_1} \tag{5.4}$$

Substituting F_{AC} in Equation (5.3) and solving for F_{BC} gives:

$$F_{BC} = \frac{mg}{\sin\theta_2 + \dfrac{\cos\theta_2}{\cos\theta_1}\sin\theta_1} \tag{5.5}$$

◁▷

Substituting $m = 100$ kg, $g = 9.81$ m s^{-2}, $\theta_1 = 60°$ and $\theta_2 = 30°$ in Equation (5.5) gives $F_{BC} = 490.5$ N. Then, using Equation (5.4), $F_{AC} = 849.6$ N.

The analysis of static systems involves, as in the above example, selecting an appropriate FBD; you can then find the unknown force by using the principles of equilibrium to relate that unknown force to other known forces acting on the isolated body. Of course, there is a certain skill, to be gained by practice, in choosing the right FBD to make the equilibrium analysis easy. I did not choose to use the free-body diagrams of the eyebolts at the ceiling in the above example, because in either case that would have left me with two unknown forces – and no known force – in each FBD, as you can see in Figure 5.15. Here, R_A and R_B are the reaction forces that the forces in the cables exert on the ceiling, in accord with Newton's Third Law. The reaction forces are there to counteract the weight of the crate. So, the external forces to a body can be of two kinds: the applied forces and the reaction forces. If we take the whole system of Figure 5.12, without breaking it into smaller bodies, the reaction forces shown in Figure 5.15 should be there to balance the weight force.

In Figure 5.15, I have drawn the reaction forces acting in the opposite direction to the forces in the

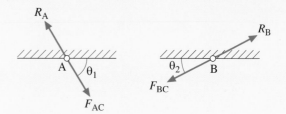

Figure 5.15   Free-body diagrams of the eyebolts at points A and B of Figure 5.12

cables. This is acceptable if there is only one force acting on the body; the reaction force should be opposite in direction and equal in magnitude to the applied force. However, if there is more than one force acting then it is usually difficult to predict the direction and magnitude of the reaction force; therefore, it is better to draw the components of the reaction forces in xy-coordinates.

EXERCISE 5.2

Find the xy-components of the reaction forces at the ceiling in the above example given in Figure 5.12. (Redraw the free-body diagrams of Figure 5.15, showing the components of all the forces in xy-coordinates.) Check that the summation of the reaction forces that you calculated balances with the weight of the crate.

☑ Equilibrium of moments

In addition to the condition that forces hold a motionless body in *translational equilibrium,* static equilibrium requires that there is also no rotation. Even if the forces acting on a body are balanced in the x- and y-directions, they may cause *angular* acceleration if they are not concurrent, i.e. they do not act through the same point. Therefore, an additional relationship between the forces is required if a body is to be in *rotational equilibrium*. In order to establish what this relationship is, we need to consider the turning effect of forces.

If you have ever wielded a spanner, you will realize that a turning effect on a nut can be achieved by

applying only one force, as illustrated in Figure 5.16. The force F applied at the handle imparts two forces on the nut: a direct force and a turning force, as represented by the force arrows with dashed lines. The direct force on the nut has the same magnitude and direction as the force applied at the handle. The turning effect is called the *moment of the force* (generally abbreviated to 'moment') and is usually denoted by M. The moment of the force depends on the magnitude of the force and the perpendicular distance between the line of action of the force and the centre of the nut, so $M = Fl$, where l is called the *moment arm*. The units of a moment arise from the definition: newton metres (N m).

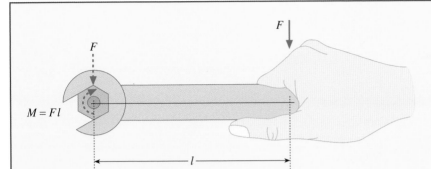

Figure 5.16   The force applied at the handle of a spanner can be equivalent to a moment and a direct force at the nut

Some moments do not arise from the application of a single force, but are exerted as a pure 'twisting effect', as occurs when you are turning a screwdriver. A 'twisting force' such as this is known as a *torque*. As you grip the screwdriver handle you are not applying a force at a single point, because the applied force is distributed by your hand around the contours of the screwdriver handle. Torque, by definition, is given in newton metres (N m) and, therefore, can and should be combined with other moments to determine the equilibrium state.

In Figure 5.16, the force is causing the nut to rotate in a *clockwise* direction; in other words, the *direction of the rotation* is clockwise. As a sign convention, we take the moments causing anticlockwise rotations as positive and clockwise rotations as negative. I will demonstrate the use of moments and rotational equilibrium with the help of the wheelbarrow shown in Figure 5.17(a), which is loaded with garden refuse of weight W. As I do not want to hurt my back, I want to know how much upward force F_{Cy} I need to apply to support the wheelbarrow.

The FBD of the barrow in given in Figure 5.17(b). As you can see, I have shown only the outline of the wheelbarrow, and I have not included the wheel in the diagram, just the components of the force exerted by the wheel on the body of the barrow. Now, I have three unknown forces, i.e. F_{Cy}, R_{Ax} and R_{Ay}, and a known force W. By choosing my xy reference frame naturally as vertical and horizontal, as shown in Figure 5.17(b), and applying translational equilibrium, I do not need to worry about the line of action of the forces,

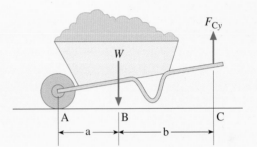

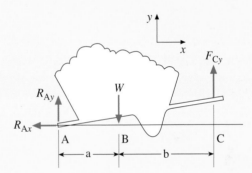

Figure 5.17   (a) Wheelbarrow and (b) associated free-body diagram

but only their magnitude and direction. First, the summation of all the forces acting in the x-direction must be equal to zero, i.e.:

$$\sum F_x = 0$$
$$-R_{Ax} = 0$$

For the y-direction:

$$\sum F_y = 0$$
$$F_{Cy} + R_{Ay} - W = 0$$

I have found one of the unknowns, $R_{Ax} = 0$.

Perhaps you anticipated this earlier – it was fairly obvious; because F_{Cy} and W are both vertical, as specified, then naturally the third force at the wheel support will have to be vertical too, so that there is no horizontal component. I am left with one equation, $F_{Cy} + R_{Ay} - W = 0$, containing two unknowns. So translational equilibrium is not enough to solve this problem, as it offers only two equations, i.e. the first two relations given in Equation (5.1), whereas I need three, i.e. as many equations as there are unknowns.

To make further progress, I must use the fact that *the barrow is in rotational equilibrium* to obtain another equation. This is the third relation in Equation (5.1), $\sum M_P = 0$, stating that the sum of the moments about a common point P should be zero. The question now arises: about what point do we take the moments? Actually, in statics we can use any point that we like. However, some points are much more convenient than others. So how do I decide which point to take moments about? I choose the point on the line of action of the force that I want to avoid. As I want to know the force on the handle, F_{Cy}, I take moments about A. This eliminates the unknown force, R_{Ay} (and R_{Ax} too, even if it were not zero) as these forces act through point A and therefore the moment arms are zero, i.e. $R_{Ay} \times 0 = 0$. So taking moments about A (remember anticlockwise rotation gives positive moment):

$$\sum M_A = 0$$
$$-W \times a + F_{Cy} \times (a + b) = 0$$

Therefore:

$$F_{Cy} = \frac{Wa}{a + b}$$

Substituting some typical values into this equation, e.g. $W = 600$ N, $a = 0.4$ m and $b = 0.8$ m, gives:

$$F_{Cy} = \frac{600\,\text{N} \times 0.4\,\text{m}}{1.2\,\text{m}} = 200\,\text{N}$$

Remember that I had three unknowns originally, which require three independent equations for their solution. Two equations were provided by translational equilibrium and one more by rotational equilibrium. I can solve for three such unknowns by obtaining three equations in that way. The wheelbarrow problem is complete because I had:

$$F_{Cy} + R_{Ay} - W = 0$$

Thus:

$$R_{Ay} = W - F_{Cy}$$
$$= 600\,\text{N} - 200\,\text{N} = 400\,\text{N}$$

The above method, i.e. using translational equilibrium plus rotational equilibrium, is a reliable way to solve simple static problems. However, it is often possible to obtain the solution more quickly by using rotational equilibrium about more than one pivot point. If I had been interested in finding R_{Ay} only, I could have taken moments about C, the point of intersection of F_{Cy} and R_{Ax}:

$$\sum M_C = 0$$
$$-R_{Ay}(a + b) + Wb = 0$$

Therefore:

$$R_{Ay} = \frac{Wb}{a + b} = \frac{600\,\text{N} \times 0.8\,\text{m}}{1.2\,\text{m}} = 400\,\text{N}$$

Naturally, this agrees with the answer obtained by the previous method.

EXERCISE 5.3

For the following examples, suggest which structural classification describes each most appropriately:

(a) the wing of an aircraft *beam*

(b) the roof of a car *plate or shell*

(c) the concrete road bridge shown in Figure 5.18. *beam*

Figure 5.18 A typical concrete road bridge; in the background is a *transporter bridge*, a rare sight as there are fewer than ten in use in the world today

SAQ 5.1 (Learning outcome 5.1)

Outline the stress distribution you would expect in the following structures or components:

(a) a cable supporting the deck of a suspension bridge *Tension*

(b) a lintel above a doorway in a brick wall *tensile bottom & compression top*

(c) the dome of a nuclear reactor, where the interior of the dome is maintained at a slightly reduced atmospheric pressure to ensure safety in the event of a leak. *Compressed by the air pressure outside.*

3 PIN-JOINTED STRUCTURES

3.1 Structures and joints

As noted earlier, trusses are commonly used in both bridges and roof structures. Figure 5.19 shows a fairly typical wooden roof-support structure used in UK housing. It clearly has a truss structure and is commonly referred to as a *roof truss*. The roof truss is designed to carry the weight of the roof cladding plus additional loads due to wind, snow, etc. So, the external load is applied over the entire upper beam as a *distributed load*, as illustrated in Figure 5.20. The load is then transferred into the other members of the structure through *joints*. In a real structure, these joints are rigidly fixed using nails, glue or gusset plates. This causes a combination of axial forces, shear forces and bending moments in the members of the structure (plus torsional forces for the general three-dimensional case). To model all these interactions accurately would be very complex and would almost certainly need to utilize numerical techniques such as finite element modelling to solve the large number of equations involved.

There would be very little point, however, in performing such sophisticated calculations, since wooden structures and joints have a high degree of variability: think of variations in the wood grain, the presence of knot holes, glue, nails, etc. The resultant variability would negate the advantages of performing a highly accurate structural analysis calculation. That said, we do need to estimate the forces in the members so that their size can be designed to be appropriate to the load they take. So in this case, it is acceptable to use a simple model of the truss.

Figure 5.19 Typical wooden roof-support structure used in houses

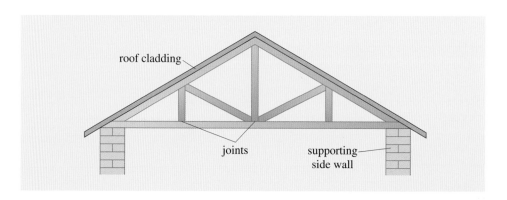

Figure 5.20 The joints in a roof truss are rigidly fixed with gusset plates and the external load is distributed over the top beam

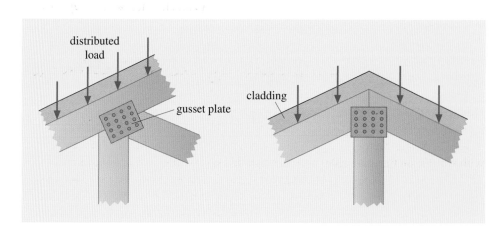

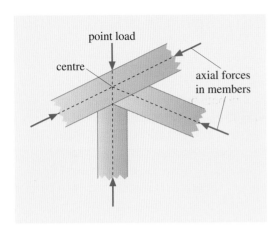

Figure 5.21   Idealization of the loading at a roof truss point

The simplest model that can be applied is where members are primarily subjected to axial forces, so the bending moments and shear forces can be neglected in the calculations. For this to be an acceptable assumption in the case of the roof truss, two conditions have to be met: the centre-lines of the members need to be *concurrent* at the joints and the external forces must be applied at the joints as *point loads*, as shown in Figure 5.21. Note that because the lines of action of the concurrent forces meet at the centre of the joint, they are unable to impose any turning moments on the joint.

In reality, these are not unreasonable assumptions to make for our roof truss. Truss structures are often designed to carry predominantly axial forces, even though some members may be subjected to bending moments. Furthermore, external loads are often applied directly at the joints as shown in Figure 5.22(a), where the weight of the roof cladding is transferred to the truss joint through a horizontal cross-beam (i.e. horizontal in the *z*-direction, out of the page). This type of load transfer at the joints is also very common in bridge trusses, where the roadway (the deck) is supported by cross-beams sitting directly at the joints of the truss structure (Figure 5.22b). Such a joint, which transfers axial forces but not bending moments, is known as a *pinned connection*, or *pin joint* (Figure 5.23). An ideal (i.e. frictionless) pinned connection prevents translational movements between members in a structure, but allows rotations; thus, the forces in the members are either tensile or compressive, and bending within the members is eliminated.

We can make further simplifications to our structural model. Since, at this stage, we are interested only in the magnitude and direction of axial forces in the members, not the corresponding stresses, we do not need information about the detail of the members themselves. That is, we do not need information on the thickness, or cross sections, of the members, and they can be represented simply by lines. Thus, Figure 5.24 gives a model of our roof-support structure where the small circles represent the pin joints. Other symbols in the figure represent contact points with the ground, or with another structure, through which forces are transmitted. The left-hand-side support with ground markings represents a *pinned support*, fixed to the ground. The little trolley with wheels, on the other side, indicates that this support allows some movement in the horizontal direction, so that it does not transmit any horizontal force. This type of support is sometimes called a *roller support*. I will explain the significance of these two types of support in Section 3.2 when we analyse these structures.

Figure 5.22   (a) The weight of the roof cladding is transferred to the truss at the joint; (b) cross-beams that sit directly on the joints of the truss structure are used to support the roadway on a bridge

The pin-jointed structure (PJS) idealization, in which the members are joined at their ends by pin joints to form a rigid structure, is the simplest *structural model* available. As well as roof-support structures, some bridge types can be idealized as pin-jointed structures. Experience has shown that, as long as the loads are applied at the joints, the bending and shear forces will be negligibly small. Thus,

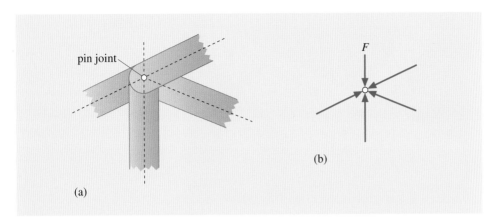

Figure 5.23   Idealization of the truss point shown in Figure 5.21 as a pin joint

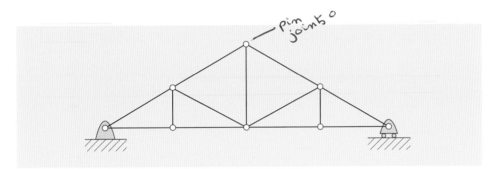

Figure 5.24   Idealization of the roof truss shown in Figure 5.19 as a pin-jointed structure

PJS idealizations of trusses usually give reasonably accurate estimates of forces in members and are relatively easy to analyse. In fact, a truss structure in which the members are joined with pins is safer than one with rigid joints, because the pin joints will not permit bending moments to develop to dangerous levels when the structure deforms slightly owing to loading or changes in temperature. In practice, though, the cost of producing pinned joints is very high compared with connecting members by traditional methods using nails, bolts, welding or gusset plates (Figure 5.25a). Hence, pin joints are usually warranted only in special cases where the movements of the structure need to be absorbed, such as the supports of large structures, as shown in Figures 5.25(b) and (c).

In Section 3.2 you will learn how to work through the analysis of a PJS, such as the model of a roof truss in Figure 5.24, in order to find the forces in the members resulting from the external loads. Once the magnitude and direction of the forces are known, individual members can then be designed accordingly. These designs can be examined, if necessary, by using the stress-analysis techniques of the previous parts in this block.

First, though, the following example illustrates how to idealize a simple structure as a PJS.

At this point I must make a clarification on the term *truss*, which is often used to describe PJS models in some textbooks. A real truss structure, however, may not necessarily be composed of pin joints, so I will not use the term truss to describe a PJS in this course.

(a)

(b)   (c)

Figure 5.25   (a) Gusset plate in a bridge truss; (b) roof support in a public building; (c) support of a bridge

EXAMPLE

Figure 5.26 shows a jib crane. Sketch a simple PJS model for determining the main forces in the jib and in the cable (labelled AB).

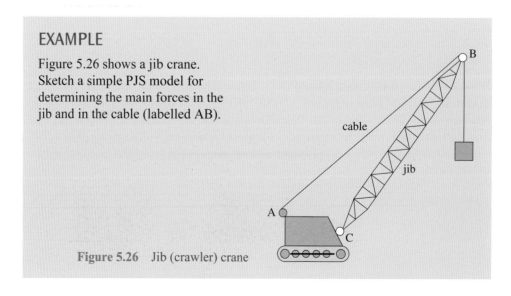

Figure 5.26   Jib (crawler) crane

SOLUTION

You might be tempted to start by representing every member in the jib in the PJS model. But, we need to find the force that the *jib* is subjected to, rather than the forces in each individual member of the jib. There is a single line of force provided from A to B by the cable: we can show the structure between B and C as a single line as well, neglecting the jib structure entirely. The forces at B and C will not change if the number or orientation of members in the jib is altered.

An appropriate idealization of the jib crane is shown in Figure 5.27, with the jib simplified as a single line. This analysis would give the force in the jib as a whole, i.e. the force transmitted by the jib from the joint B to the joint C.

If the magnitudes of the forces in each member of the jib were required, they would have to be analysed by considering each joint in the jib as a pin joint, and our simplification would not be appropriate.

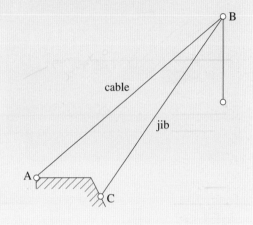

Figure 5.27 Idealization of jib crane as a pin-jointed structure

The previous example shows how the structure between two pin joints can effectively be ignored when what is required is just the force transmitted from one joint to the other.

PJS idealization is commonly used when analysing truss bridges. Look at the bridge structure shown in Figure 5.28. Here, the individual members are rigidly connected by bolts and welding, so there may be some bending induced by the loads on the bridge. However, since the roadway sits directly on the joints, the members are predominantly loaded by axial forces and the bending moments can be ignored.

EXAMPLE

Sketch a simple two-dimensional PJS idealization of the bridge shown in Figure 5.28 for the purpose of determining the forces in the members of the structures.

Figure 5.28 Truss bridge structure

SOLUTION

If you look at the bridge carefully, you'll notice that the bridge is constructed from a pair of plane trusses joined together using cross-beams at the lower joints of each plane truss. The roadway sits directly on these cross-beams, so that the load is divided between two plane trusses. (This type of configuration is known as a *pony truss bridge*.) Therefore, we need to analyse only one of the plane trusses. Figure 5.29(a) shows how the rigid joints in one of the plane trusses are idealized as pin joints, as superimposed on the bridge photograph. I have redrawn the PJS in Figure 5.29(b) as an FBD for clarity.

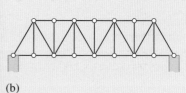

(b)

(a)

Figure 5.29   (a) Pin-jointed structure (PJS) and (b) free-body diagram of the truss bridge

SAQ 5.2 (Learning outcome 5.2)

For the structure shown in Figure 5.30, sketch an idealized two-dimensional PJS.

Figure 5.30   Truss bridge

The symmetrical nature of bridge trusses such as those shown in Figures 5.28–5.30 allows them to be treated as two-dimensional pin-jointed structures. Even if the loading is not distributed evenly between plane trusses that form the structure, each plane truss can in theory be analysed separately as long as the external loading at each truss is known. Next, I will show you how two-dimensional pin-jointed structures are analysed to find the forces in each member as a result of external loads on the structure. I shall consider only the cases where the external loading is applied directly at the pin joints.

3.2 Analysis of pin-jointed structures

The basic element of a PJS is a triangle, because three members joined by pins constitute a rigid frame. Understanding how a triangular pin-jointed element carries an external load is the first step in the analysis of pin-jointed structures. Figure 5.31 shows a triangular PJS with a point load at the top joint. If we are to design a structure based on this, we need to determine the internal force in each individual member, so that the appropriate size and shape of these members can be chosen for construction.

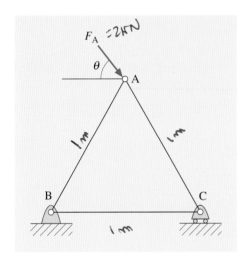

Figure 5.31 An equilateral triangular PJS, subjected to a load at a joint; all members are 1 m in length

Constructing an appropriate FBD is an essential first step in the analysis of pin-jointed structures. You have already seen how to use the equilibrium conditions on an FBD of a single pin (or an eyebolt) to find the unknown forces exerted on it. This is the basis of the *method of joints*, where the whole PJS is analysed by working through it pin by pin. If the forces in only one or more members are needed, rather than all of them, it is often quicker to choose an FBD comprising several members and pins together. You cut out a free body that is not just a single pin, but a larger portion of the PJS. This second method is called the *method of sections*. The best choice of free body depends upon the problem in hand.

Note that in the analysis of pin-jointed stuctures in this section I will neglect friction at the pins. Also, the weight of the members is neglected, although often it can be incorporated simply by adding forces at the pins.

3.3 The method of joints

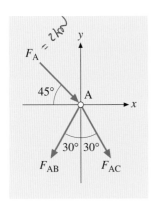

Figure 5.32 Free-body diagram of pin A

Let's analyse the simple triangular PJS shown in Figure 5.31 for the conditions where $\theta = 45°$ and $F_A = 2$ kN. I will start from a pin, apply the equilibrium conditions to find the unknown forces and repeat the same procedures at all pins one by one. Obviously, the starting pin ought to be the one where the known external force is applied.

Figure 5.32 shows the FBD of pin A where the external load is applied. I have drawn an xy reference frame on the diagram, taking the pin as the origin. Note that I have drawn the forces in the members AB and AC, labelled F_{AB} and F_{AC} respectively, pointing away from the pin, as if they are pulling. This is the common way of representing *tensile* forces in members; the reason for this sign convention is that a tensile *internal* force in a member pulls inwards, reacting against the external loads that are causing it to stretch.

Of course, I have no idea at this stage whether the members are in tension or compression. The convention is to assume that all the forces are in tension to begin with. If this assumption is <u>incorrect</u>, and a member is really in compression, then the <u>equilibrium equation will result in a negative value for that force</u>. I am going to stick to this convention, and presume that both forces in Figure 5.32 are in tension to start with, and mark the force arrows accordingly.

Now, applying the equilibrium equations:

$$\sum F_x = 0$$
$$F_A \cos 45° - F_{AB} \cos 60° + F_{AC} \cos 60° = 0 \qquad (5.6a)$$

and

$$\sum F_y = 0$$
$$-F_A \sin 45° - F_{AB} \cos 30° - F_{AC} \cos 30° = 0 \qquad (5.6b)$$

So, we have two equations for two unknowns. Substituting the values and rearranging Equation (5.6a) gives:

$$2 \text{ kN} \times 0.707 - F_{AB} \times 0.5 + F_{AC} \times 0.5 = 0$$

Thus:

$$F_{AB} = F_{AC} + 2.83 \text{ kN}$$

Remember, when we apply the equilibrium conditions, we are equilibrating the forces acting on the *pin* and therefore the sign of the force in the equation depends only on the direction of the force in the reference frame. For example, the x-component of F_{AB} in Equation (5.6a) takes a negative sign because it points in the negative x-direction.

Substituting this into Equation (5.6b) gives:

$$-2\text{ kN} \times 0.707 - \left(F_{AC} + 2.83\text{ kN}\right) \times 0.866 - F_{AC} \times 0.866 = 0$$

Therefore:

$$F_{AC} = -2.23\text{ kN}$$

F_{AB} is then calculated as:

$$F_{AB} = F_{AC} + 2.83\text{ kN}$$
$$= -2.23\text{ kN} + 2.83\text{ kN}$$
$$= +0.60\text{ kN}$$

The results show that I did choose the right direction for F_{AB}, but not for F_{AC}. So, member AB is indeed in tension, but member AC is in compression, as shown in Figure 5.33.

When finding unknown forces at the pins, it is possible to choose the reference frame in such a way that the calculations become a bit easier. For simplicity in this example I used a standard xy reference frame, but if I had chosen one of the reference directions, say the x'-axis, aligned with one of the unknown forces, say F_{AC}, as shown in Figure 5.34, then F_{AC} would have been eliminated from the equilibrium equation in the perpendicular direction, i.e. the y'-axis.

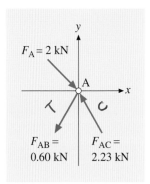

Figure 5.33 Magnitude and direction of forces at pin A

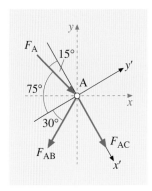

Figure 5.34 New reference frame for the free-body diagram of pin A

EXERCISE 5.4

Using the reference frame of Figure 5.34, check that the calculation gives the same results as above.

There is only one more member in which the magnitude and the direction of the force are unknown, i.e. member BC. I am going to calculate the force in this member by considering the force equilibrium at pin C. You may rightfully ask, why not pin B? Well, it is to do with the unknown reaction forces at the supports. The support at B is a *pinned* support, which prevents movements in vertical and horizontal directions, but allows the members to rotate. The reaction provided by this type of support, as can be seen in Figure 5.35(a), is a force R_G inclined at some angle θ to the horizontal. However, it is usually simpler to resolve this force into its components in vertical and horizontal axes, as in Figure 5.35(b). In both cases, though, there are two unknowns: either the single force R_G plus the angle θ, or two forces, R_{Gx} and R_{Gy}, aligned with the known reference frame.

The roller support in Figure 5.35(c), on the other hand, is free to move horizontally, allows rotations to members attached to it, but is restrained in the vertical direction. Therefore, it provides only a vertical reaction; that means only one unknown.

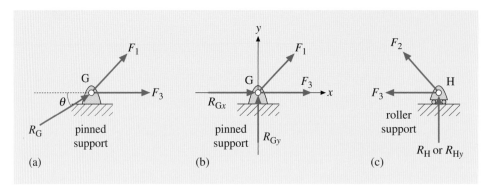

Figure 5.35   Pinned and roller supports

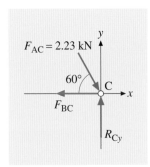

Figure 5.36   Free-body diagram of pin C

The FBD of pin C is shown in Figure 5.36. There is a horizontal force on the pin from member BC of the PJS, but there is no horizontal reaction force: the force in BC will be balanced by the horizontal component of the force in AC.

Hence, there are two unknowns at pin C: the force in member BC and the vertical reaction force at the pin. Note that the magnitude and direction of the force in member AC, i.e. F_{AC}, are now known from the analysis of pin A above. Since it was found that F_{AC} puts member AC in compression, the same sense of direction should also be taken in Figure 5.36, and hence F_{AC} acts towards the pin. I chose the direction of F_{BC} to be tensile and the direction of the reaction force R_{Cy} to be upwards; if I guess wrongly, then the mathematics will give it a negative sign automatically.

Applying the equilibrium equations, along the y-axis:

$$\sum F_y = 0$$
$$-F_{AC}\sin 60° + R_{Cy} = 0$$

Therefore:

$$R_{Cy} = 2.23 \text{ kN} \times \sin 60° = 1.93 \text{ kN}$$

Applying equilibrium along the x-axis:

$$\sum F_x = 0$$
$$F_{AC}\cos 60° - F_{BC} = 0$$

Therefore:

$$F_{BC} = 2.23 \text{ kN} \times \cos 60° = 1.12 \text{ kN}$$

We now know all the forces in the members. However, we haven't finished the analysis yet. There are two unknown reaction forces left in support B (Figure 5.37).

Applying equilibrium along the y-axis:

$$\sum F_y = 0$$
$$R_{By} + 0.60 \text{ kN} \times \cos 30° = 0$$

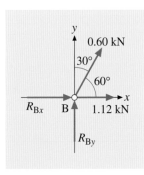

Figure 5.37   Free-body diagram of pin B

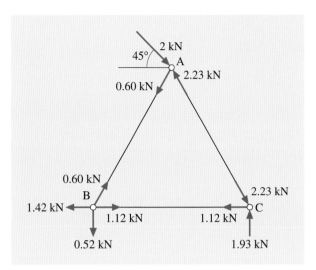

Figure 5.38 Magnitude and direction of forces in the triangular pin-jointed structure

Therefore:

$$R_{By} = -0.52 \text{ kN}$$

Applying equilibrium along the x-axis:

$$\sum F_x = 0$$
$$R_{Bx} + 0.6 \text{ kN} \times \cos 60° + 1.12 \text{ kN} = 0$$

So:

$$R_{Bx} = -1.42 \text{ kN}$$

Both R_{By} and R_{Bx} are negative, meaning that their direction is opposite to my assumed direction.

A convenient way to summarize the results of a PJS analysis such as this is to superimpose the pin free-body diagrams onto the structure diagram, as in Figure 5.38.

SAQ 5.3 (Learning outcome 5.3)

Study the results of the structural analysis of the triangular PJS given in Figure 5.38.

(a) What type of force (i.e. tensile or compressive) is each member subjected to?

AB & BC in tension
AC compression

(b) What are the forces exerted by the structure on the supports at B and C?

0.52 kN↑   1.42 kN→   1.93 kN↓

(c) What total force does the truss exert on its supports?

2 kN

It is not always desirable, or even possible, to work right through the structure from the known applied forces. It is usually better to calculate the supporting (reaction)

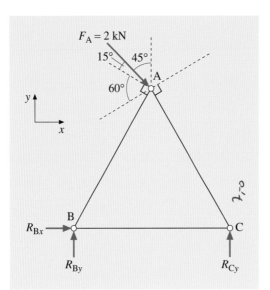

Figure 5.39 Free-body diagram of whole truss to find the reaction forces; members are 1 m long

forces first. To do this you need to choose the complete truss as the free body, as in Figure 5.39. As before, the nature of the individual supports indicates that we must show a horizontal and a vertical component at B and only a vertical component at C.

Here there are three unknowns, but unlike the case of individual pins, we can use rotational equilibrium too. This is possible as the forces are not concurrent. So, applying translational equilibrium in two directions and a rotational equilibrium about any convenient point should give us three equations that can be juggled to give the unknown forces. Careful choice of direction or moment points would keep the solution simple.

First, taking moments about B automatically eliminates two unknowns from the equation:

$$\sum M_B = 0$$
$$\left(R_{Cy} \times 1 \text{ m}\right) - \left(F_A \cos 15° \times 1 \text{ m}\right) = 0$$

Therefore:

$$R_{Cy} = 2 \text{ kN} \times \cos 15° = 1.93 \text{ kN}$$

Two translational equilibrium equations would then give the two unknown reaction forces at B:

$$\sum F_x = 0$$
$$R_{Bx} + F_A \sin 45° = 0$$

Thus:

$$R_{Bx} = -2 \text{ kN} \times \cos 45° = -1.41 \text{ kN}$$

And:

$$\sum F_y = 0$$
$$R_{By} + R_{Cy} - F_A \cos 45° = 0$$

Thus:

$$R_{By} = -1.93 \text{ kN} + 2 \text{ kN} \times \cos 45° = -0.52 \text{ kN}$$

These results agree with those found earlier (except for a small rounding error in the case of R_{Bx}).

SAQ 5.4 (Learning outcome 5.3)

Apply rotational equilibrium about point C of Figure 5.39 to find R_{By} and compare with the above result obtained using translational equilibrium.

(handwritten annotation:)
$\Sigma \Pi c = 0$
$-(F_A \cos 75° \times 1m)$
$\quad -(R_{By} \times 1m) = 0$
$R_{By} = -0.52 kN$

In this simple example of a PJS it was possible, although perhaps a little tedious, to use the method of joints exclusively and then to find the supporting reactions just as a final check. In many cases it is not possible to work that way round. For example, look at the PJS given in Figure 5.40. Is it possible to use equilibrium at pin C or E, where a known load is applied, to solve for any unknown forces in the members?

No, it is not. There are three unknown concurrent forces at pin C, which are too many to solve directly by equilibrium at pins. What we must do is find the supporting forces on the whole truss first by applying translational and rotational equilibrium. Then we can start at a pin such as D, where there will be two unknowns, F_{CD} and F_{DE}. This tells us the force F_{CD} in member CD, so at C there are now only two unknowns, and F_{BC} and F_{CE} can be found. By choosing the right order to deal with the pins you will be faced with only one or two unknowns at each pin.

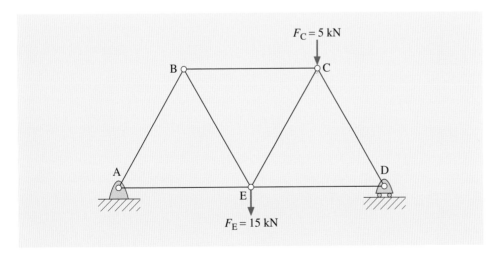

Figure 5.40 PJS of a seven-member truss; all members are 1 m long

SAQ 5.5 (Learning outcome 5.3)

With the help of the instructions given above, find the forces in the members and at the supports of the PJS given in Figure 5.40.

SAQ 5.6 (Learning outcomes 5.3 and 5.4)

Figure 5.41 shows a PJS of a short bridge truss. Find the reaction at C and the force in members BC and BE. Do note that a triangle with three equal sides must also have three equal angles of 60°.

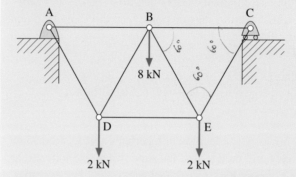

Figure 5.41   Bridge truss; all members are 2 m long

SAQ 5.7 (Learning outcomes 5.3 and 5.4)

Use the method of joints to find the forces in each member of the structure in Figure 5.42.

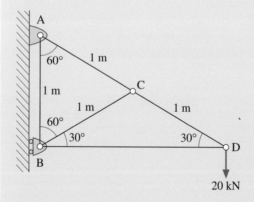

Figure 5.42   Gantry

3.4 The method of sections

The method of joints is a quite straightforward and simple method, but can be rather tedious to carry out. Suppose that in the example structure of Figure 5.40 we wanted to know the force in member BC only. Do we really need to work pin by pin through the structure to pin B or C? What if the truss contained many more members? In a complicated structure this could be a lot of work for the single result actually required.

Thankfully, it can often be done more efficiently. If the forces in only one or two members of a structure are required, it is better to make a careful choice of free body to give the required result directly. This is called the method of sections, because the structure is 'sectioned' at an appropriate place.

However, before we use the method of sections, we need the external forces acting on the structure as a whole, including the reaction forces. Figure 5.43 shows the FBD for the whole structure of Figure 5.40. We know from the answer to SAQ 5.5 that $R_{Dy} = 11.25$ kN, $R_{Ay} = 8.75$ kN and $R_{Ax} = 0$.

I can now apply the method of sections. To find an unknown force, say the force in member BC in Figure 5.43, we take an imaginary cut through the section and then solve for the forces on the FBD of the section. The cut must pass through the member of interest, to 'expose' the internal force.

I could take a section through, say, members BC, BE and AE. Naturally, I must cut through the force that I want to know (F_{BC}), but inevitably I shall expose other unknown forces in BE and AE by the cut I have chosen. I have shown both halves of the sectioned bodies in Figure 5.44.

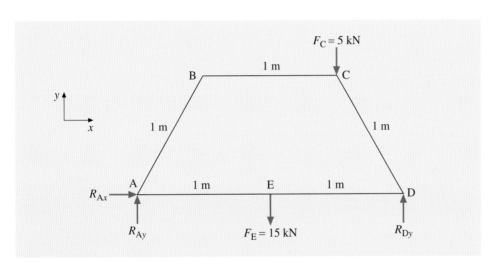

Figure 5.43 Free-body diagram for the whole structure of Figure 5.40

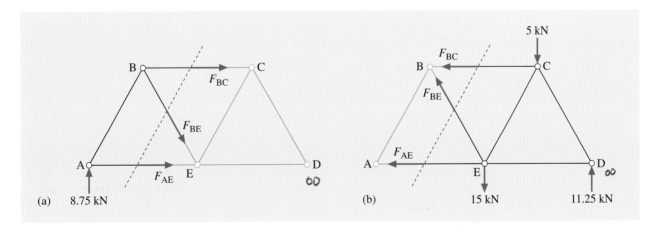

Figure 5.44 Method of sections

I have marked the exposed unknown forces as being in tension. I could work with either half of the structure as my free body. Naturally, I would choose the simpler piece. Ideally, I would like to use the equilibrium condition to obtain an equation involving F_{BC} but not F_{BE} or F_{AE}. A close examination reveals that F_{BE} and F_{AE} are concurrent forces at pin E. So, if I take moments about E, then these two unknowns will not be in the equation, and the only unknown will be F_{BC}.

Does it matter which half of the section I take? No, as the point about which you take moments does not have to be a point on the free body itself. However, the use of the right-hand section involves three external forces, whereas the left-hand one involves only one external support force, so I would choose that one.

Applying moment equilibrium about pin E in Figure 5.44(a) gives:

Note that the shortest distance between pin E and the line of action of F_{BC} equals 1 m × sin 60°.

$$\sum M_E = 0$$
$$-(8.75 \text{ kN} \times 1 \text{ m}) - (F_{BC} \times 0.866 \text{ m}) = 0$$

Therefore:

$$F_{BC} = -10.10 \text{ kN}$$

as we found in the answer to SAQ 5.5 using the method of joints.

EXERCISE 5.5

Use the section given in Figure 5.44(b) to find the force F_{BC}, and compare it with the above result.

SAQ 5.8 (Learning outcomes 5.3 and 5.4)

By using the method of sections, find the force in member CF in the roof truss given in Figure 5.45, assuming it is a PJS with a pin joint at A and a roller support at B. Repeat the calculation by using the method of joints.

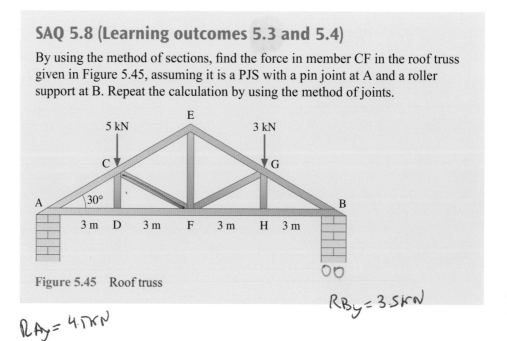

Figure 5.45 Roof truss

$R_{Ay} = 4.5 kN$

$R_{By} = 3.5 kN$

SAQ 5.9 (Learning outcomes 5.3 and 5.4)

The weight of the deck and load due to traffic on a truss bridge are assumed to transfer to the lower joints of the structure as equally shared loads, as shown in Figure 5.46. Find the forces in members EF and CD using the method of sections.

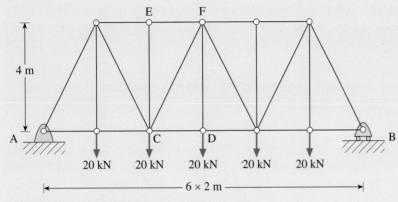

Figure 5.46   Truss bridge

4 THE DETERMINACY OF STRUCTURES

I must confess that I haven't been playing fair with the analysis of all the pin-jointed structures in Part 5 so far. I have selected the examples very carefully such that all the problems were solvable. That is, there were just as many unknown forces in the structures as there were independent equilibrium equations. Such structures are called *statically determinate structures*.

If there are not enough equations to enable us to find all the forces in the members, then the structure is called *statically indeterminate*. As an example, consider the triangular PJS that we studied earlier (Figure 5.31), reproduced in Figure 5.47 with one difference: the roller support is replaced with a second pinned support.

With this configuration, there is one additional constraint at pin C, which increases the number of unknown reaction forces to four. Together with the internal forces in the members, there are now seven unknowns. Can we still analyse the PJS with the methods we have learned to find the unknown forces? Let's see! Using the method of joints at pin A we can still find the forces in members AB and AC, as before. However, the difficulty arises when we try to determine the forces at pins B and C (Figure 5.48). In each case there are three unknowns, but only two equilibrium equations (i.e. $\sum F_x = 0$ and $\sum F_y = 0$) are available. Even if we take the whole structure as a free body and apply the rotational equilibrium equation ($\sum M = 0$) in addition to the translational ones, we have one too many unknowns.

It seems that if the number of constraints (reactions) on a body at static equilibrium is greater than three, then the body must be statically indeterminate, since we can set only three independent equilibrium equations. But this is not always true for pin-jointed structures: we may have fewer unknown member forces. For example,

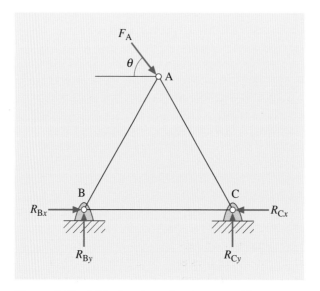

Figure 5.47 PJS of a triangular element with two pinned supports

if we remove the member BC from the PJS of Figure 5.47, the structure becomes statically determinate again. We can now solve for the reaction forces in the free-body diagrams in Figure 5.48, because we can discount the unknown F_{BC}.

Fortunately, there is a systematic approach where one can test the determinacy of pin-jointed structures. We can formularize the number of unknowns and number of independent equations in a PJS. The number of unknowns in a PJS is equal to the number of reactions plus the number of members (as each member carries only an axial force). In a PJS, the number of independent equations is two per joint, i.e. horizontal and vertical (translational) equilibrium equations. Since the forces at a joint are concurrent, rotational equilibrium provides no extra information for pin-jointed structures, but can give convenience in calculations.

We can write a simple equation based on the above for a determinacy test of pin-jointed structures: if m is the number of members in the PJS, r is the number of reactions and j is the number of joints (including joints at supports), then a PJS is said to be statically *determinate* when:

$$m + r = 2j \tag{5.7}$$

If $m + r > 2j$ then there are more unknowns than the available equations, so the structure is statically *indeterminate*.

If $m + r < 2j$ then there are more equations than unknown forces in the structure. This actually signifies that there is not a sufficient number of members and/or constraints to hold the structure stable. So the structure is a *mechanism*, or it is said to be *unstable*.

The determinacy test is just counting practice. Figure 5.49 applies this to some structures. You are familiar with the first two as we have already studied them above. The first one, Figure 5.49(a), should be statically determinate and the determinacy test confirms this. Constraining the structure further by adding an extra reaction force makes it indeterminate (Figure 5.49b).

Figure 5.49(c) shows a rectangular frame with cross-bracing. Although it has only three reaction forces, the structure is statically indeterminate because it has one too many members; in other words, it has a *redundant* member (hence, these types of structure are often referred to as redundant). Removing one of the braces makes the structure determinate (Figure 5.49d). This does not mean that the redundant members have no function in a structure. It only means that the static equilibrium equations alone are not sufficient to analyse the structure to find the unknown forces.

In practice, many structures are deliberately designed to be redundant, despite the fact that this makes them more difficult to analyse. This gives additional stability and safety to the structure. The failure of any member of a statically determinate structure results in a collapse of all or part of the structure. But when an indeterminate structure deforms with loading, the redundant members begin to carry some of the burden. The analysis of redundant structures requires equations developed by the consideration of *displacement compatibility* (equivalent to strain compatibility, which you were introduced to in Part 4) in addition to static equilibrium equations. We will look into this later in this part.

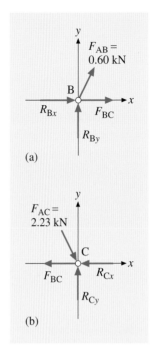

Figure 5.48   Free-body diagrams of (a) pin B and (b) pin C for the PJS of Figure 5.47

Figure 5.49   Static determinacy test

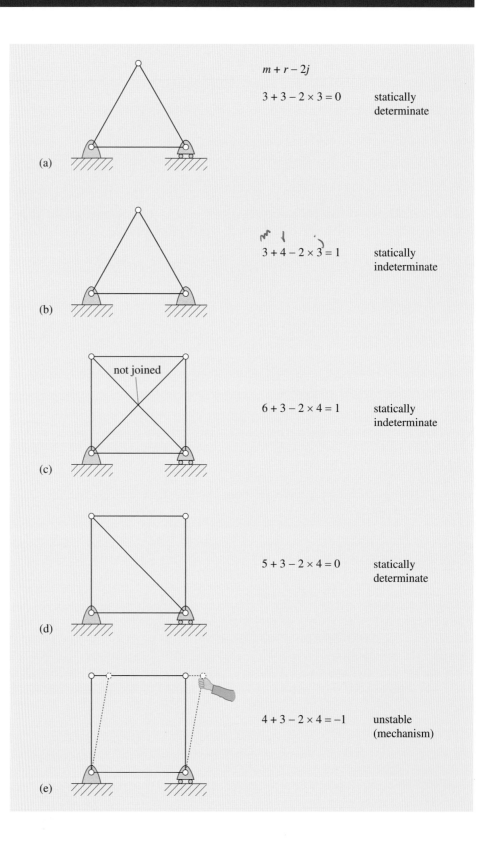

$m + r - 2j$

$3 + 3 - 2 \times 3 = 0$ statically determinate

(a)

$3 + 4 - 2 \times 3 = 1$ statically indeterminate

(b)

not joined

$6 + 3 - 2 \times 4 = 1$ statically indeterminate

(c)

$5 + 3 - 2 \times 4 = 0$ statically determinate

(d)

$4 + 3 - 2 \times 4 = -1$ unstable (mechanism)

(e)

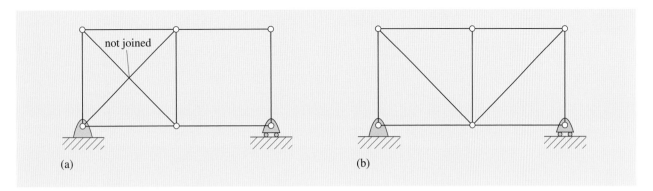

Figure 5.50   Failure of static determinacy test

The opposite of redundancy occurs when there is an <u>insufficient number of members for the structure to be stable.</u> Removing the remaining bracing of the rectangular structure in Figure 5.49(d) makes the structure a mechanism, as shown in Figure 5.49(e). There are insufficient members to maintain stability, so the structure would collapse.

You should be aware, however, that Equation (5.7) is not foolproof. It sometimes gives a wrong diagnosis on the determinacy. For example, apply the determinacy test to the PJS given in Figure 5.50(a). There are nine members, three reactions and six joints: $9 + 3 = 2 \times 6$. That is, according to Equation (5.7), this is a statically determinate structure. However, close inspection reveals that this structure is not stable at all. The right-hand rectangular element is a mechanism, whereas the left-hand double-braced element has redundancy. Although our static determinacy test tells us that apparently there are the correct numbers of members and reactions in the structure overall, for a large structure there may be features within it that mean it is not in fact statically determinate; moving one of the braces to the right-hand element makes the whole structure statically determinate (Figure 5.50b).

So, it is important not to rely on Equation (5.7) alone for testing structures for redundancy. A rule of thumb is that it is better to check all the supports and individual elements of the structure. Another rule of thumb is that triangular elements are always stable and rectangular elements are usually the source of problems.

SAQ 5.10 (Learning outcomes 5.5 and 5.6)

Determine whether the structures in Figure 5.51 are statically determinate, redundant or mechanisms. In the case of a redundant structure or mechanism, suggest a way of making the structure statically determinate by removal or addition of members or reactions.

Figure 5.51
Determinacy test

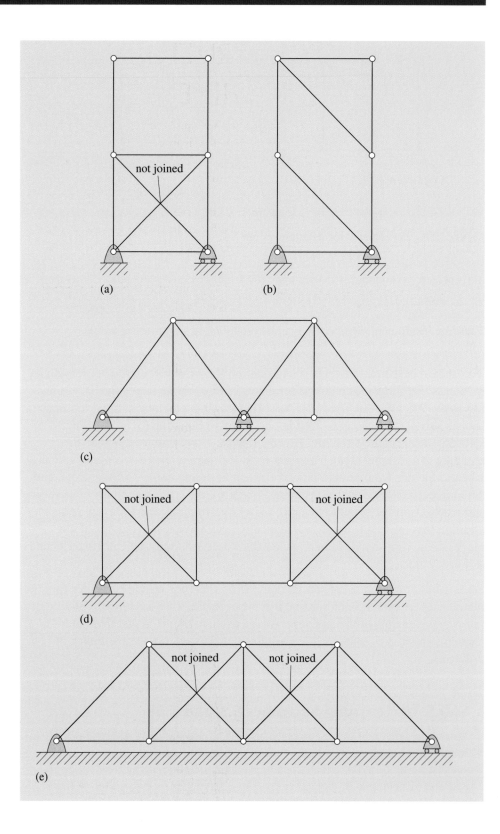

5 CASE STUDY 1: STRUCTURAL ANALYSIS OF A MACHINE

It is important to recognize that the analyses we have just gone through can be used to estimate the loads in any structure or machine that is in static equilibrium and whose geometry is amenable to being modelled as a PJS. This brings us back to an important point made earlier in Part 5 – that all structural and stress analyses are just models of reality. They may differ in their realism and potential accuracy, but none is a perfect description. In design, we introduce conservatism to ensure structural integrity. In analysis, when we are analysing the forces in a component or machine that already exists, we must be aware that the results we get are dependent on the assumptions we make.

To illustrate these points, we will look at how we can use the methods detailed above to estimate the forces to be provided by the rams on the hydraulic digger shown in Figure 5.52.

Let's say we need to estimate the forces in the hydraulic rams GF, CD and AC when the digger exerts a force of 20 kN horizontally to the right at J on the ground. To make life easier, we will neglect the weight of the rams, members and bucket.

We need to be able to assume that the digger is in static equilibrium: that is, none of its members is accelerating while it is exerting the force at point J. This is a reasonable assumption, at least for an instant before the bucket starts displacing the earth.

Acceleration means that additional forces are acting on the structure – from Newton's Second Law, $F = ma$.

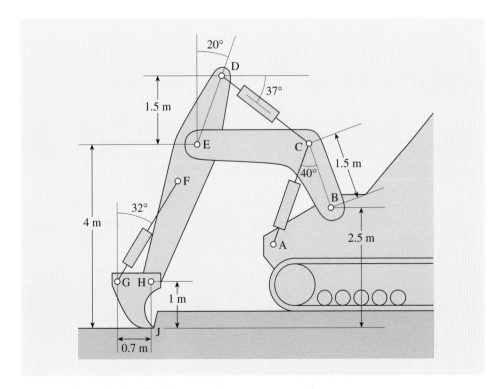

Figure 5.52   A hydraulic digger used to excavate trenches

How do we apply the pin-jointed structure idealization to the digger? Well, the digger is basically a series of lever mechanisms and pin joints. We isolate each lever and its associated pin joint separately by drawing an FBD and showing all the forces acting on it. Take, for example, the ram FG. The mechanism is such that, when the ram FG applies a force at G, the bucket pivots about the pin joint at H to counterbalance the ground force at J, assuming the rest of the digger is stationary. Figure 5.53 shows the FBD of the bucket with the applied forces on it. Note that, as this is the FBD of the bucket, the 20 kN force at J is shown as the force exerted on the bucket by the ground (Newton's Third Law).

The force in ram FG, F_{FG}, can then be calculated by taking moments about pin joint H. To do that, we need to determine the moment arms between the lines of action of all the forces that apply moment about H. Recall that the moment arm is, by definition, the perpendicular distance between the line of action of a force and the point about which the moment of the force is sought. The moment arm for the 20 kN force at J in Figure 5.53 is 1 m, since this is the shortest (and therefore perpendicular) distance between point H and the line of action of the force at J. However, the distance L_{GH} is not the moment arm of the force F_{FG}, as it is not perpendicular to the line of action of the force, making an angle of 32°. I therefore need to calculate the shortest distance between H and the line of action of F_{FG}. Alternatively, and more conveniently in this case, I can use L_{GH} as the moment arm if I resolve the force F_{FG} into its components perpendicular and parallel to L_{GH}. Since the component of the force that is parallel to the moment arm does not contribute to the moment at H, only the component of the force that is perpendicular to L_{GH} (i.e. $F_{FG} \cos 32°$) will cause a moment at H. Thus, the moment equation gives:

$$\sum M_H = 0$$
$$-(F_{FG} \cos 32° \times 0.7 \text{ m}) - (20 \text{ kN} \times 1 \text{ m}) = 0$$

Therefore:

$$F_{FG} = -33.7 \text{ kN}$$

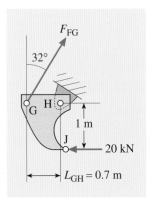

Figure 5.53 Free-body diagram of the bucket to calculate the force in ram FG; note that I have not shown the reaction forces at H, for clarity

That is, the ram FG applies a compressive force on the bucket.

To determine the force in the ram CD, we consider the pivot action about the joint E. So, we combine the digger arm DH with the ram FG and the bucket where the external force is applied and draw the FBD as shown in Figure 5.54. Note that the ram FG is now regarded as an integral part of the free body, since the two coaxial forces that the ram generates, acting on points F and G, are equal in magnitude but opposite in direction, and so sum to zero. Also note that the rest of the digger joining at E is assumed to be stationary.

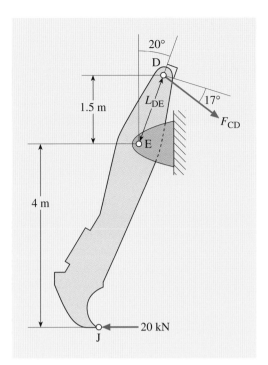

Figure 5.54   Free-body diagram of the bucket and the arm DH; note that I have not shown the reaction forces at E, for clarity

EXERCISE 5.6

Calculate the force in ram CD, using the FBD given in Figure 5.54.

SAQ 5.11 (Learning outcomes 5.4 and 5.5)

Calculate the force in ram AC by drawing an appropriate FBD.

6 THE ROLE OF COMPUTERS IN STRUCTURAL ANALYSIS

It will be no surprise that most structural analysis is now performed using computers. A wide variety of commercial software is available, and although it is possible to use many of these software packages without understanding the basic mechanics and structural theory on which they are based, it is certainly not advisable. In this section, I want to look at how the analytical methods we have been exploring in this part of the course can be adapted for use with computers.

So many computer software packages are available that using them effectively is no trivial task. Indeed, without a clear understanding of the problem to be solved and how the computer is programmed to achieve a solution, the results can be at best unreliable and at worst disastrous! I do not intend to cover any of the approaches or specific packages here. However, it is worth covering at a basic level the underlying technique used, so that armed with your knowledge of the principles of stress and structural analysis you will be able to conduct an informed discussion of any problem and solution with experts.

You will already have some idea of how computer-based structural analysis works, following our examination of 'How the finite element method works' in Block 1 Part 4. For example, you saw how it was possible to determine stresses and strains from nodal forces and displacements in a simple, one-dimensional finite element model of a stepped rod loaded in uniaxial tension. Recall that such analyses use something called a *stiffness matrix* to describe the load–displacement characteristics of a structure, based on the load–displacement characteristics of the elements into which the structure has been subdivided. Breaking down an analysis in this way is pretty much what we do when we use the method of joints to solve for forces in a statically determinate PJS. The difference here is that the stiffness matrix method uses *compatibility* and *equilibrium* to solve the problem, and the whole of the structure is considered, not just its component members one by one. It is a powerful method, and can put some quantification towards traditional engineering 'rules of thumb', such as ☑ **stiffness attracts load** ☑.

Of course, the only way in which any design can be improved or optimized is by thoroughly understanding the loads in the structure and how they are produced. Making a component or structure bigger just because it has failed is not a universal panacea.

Inevitably, this section will involve descriptions of some quite complex mathematics. However, there is no requirement for you to understand the mathematics fully or be able to reproduce it: it is there just to give you an appreciation of how these methods work.

In fact, the stiffness matrix method is used in computer software that can be applied to solve virtually all truss or framed structures (i.e. those whose load path involves primarily single members joined at their ends); in other words, all trusses independent of whether they are pin jointed, whether they contain redundant members, etc. The method is most useful for the solution of statically indeterminate structures.

To show you how this works I'll go back to the statically indeterminate PJS of a triangular truss with two pinned supports that we examined in Figure 5.47. Recall that I could not determine the four reaction forces at the supports, as I had only three independent equilibrium equations. I will show you how to obtain them using the stiffness matrix method. I have redrawn this structure using three finite elements and

☑ Stiffness attracts load

A common phrase heard amongst practising engineers is 'stiffness attracts load'. This is clearly not universally true; for example, if I have a weight hanging from a cable, making the cable stiffer (say by increasing its diameter) will not change the load on the cable, although it will reduce the displacement of the end of the cable attached to the load. The statement 'stiffness attracts load' is true for situations where there are multiple load paths (redundancy) and members that have the same displacement conditions. A common example of this is where a flat, relatively thick floor or ceiling is supported on many pillars. If the stiffness of one of the pillars is increased, then that pillar will carry proportionally more of the load and it is this fact that has led to the maxim 'stiffness attracts load'.

The basic condition that the load on a member is displacement-controlled (and hence stiffness-controlled), rather than load-controlled, is quite common in many engineering situations; and a common mistake if a component is, for example, failing by fatigue or some other load-controlled failure mechanism is to strengthen the component by making it bigger. However, this also stiffens the structure locally and can lead to increased loads so that the new design performs no better in service. In some circumstances, the performance of the component or structure can actually worsen.   △

three nodes in Figure 5.55; the truss is pinned at nodes 1 and 3, and loaded at node 2, as shown. The first thing to notice is that, obviously, this is a *two-dimensional structure*; so we need an *xy*-coordinate system to describe the forces and displacements fully. That means that there is rather more information associated with the model than would be necessary for a one-dimensional case: Figure 5.56(a) illustrates the difference between a one-dimensional model with forces and displacements in one direction only, and a two-dimensional model with forces and displacements along two axes. When considering two dimensions it is best to refer all forces and displacements to a chosen *xy*-coordinate system, so every node must be associated with a force component in the *x*-direction and a force component in the *y*-direction, e.g. F_{1x} and F_{1y} at node 1 in Figure 5.56(b). Similarly, two displacement components are required for each node in

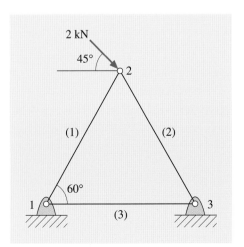

Figure 5.55   Finite model of a pin-jointed triangular truss with two pinned supports; there are three elements, labelled (1), (2) and (3), linked by three nodes, labelled 1, 2 and 3

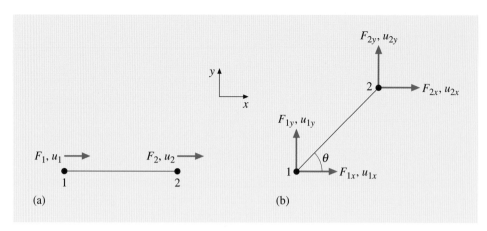

Figure 5.56   Forces and displacements for (a) one-dimensional and (b) two-dimensional finite element model

the two-dimensional case (e.g. u_{1x} and u_{1y} in Figure 5.56b). Furthermore, the angular orientation θ of the element (measured anticlockwise from the positive x-axis direction) also needs to be incorporated.

So, how do we assemble all this information? Well, recall from Block 1 Part 4 that the vector of nodal forces $\{F\}$ is related to the vector of nodal displacements $\{u\}$ using a stiffness matrix $[k]$ such that:

$$\{F\} = [k]\{u\} \tag{5.8a}$$

and for the single one-dimensional element of Figure 5.56(a) this can be written in full as:

$$\begin{Bmatrix} F_1 \\ F_2 \end{Bmatrix} = \frac{AE}{L} \begin{bmatrix} 1 & -1 \\ -1 & 1 \end{bmatrix} \begin{Bmatrix} u_1 \\ u_2 \end{Bmatrix} \tag{5.8b}$$

> Note that all the nodal forces defined in a stiffness matrix correspond to forces at joints, i.e. either externally applied loads or reaction forces at the supports, and should not be confused with the internal forces in members.

For the two-dimensional case things are a little trickier; assembling the stiffness matrix, in particular, becomes rather unwieldy. So, because I just want to give you an idea of how the analysis works for our two-dimensional truss structure, I'll simply show you what the equivalent expression for the element of Figure 5.56(b) looks like:

$$\begin{Bmatrix} F_{1x} \\ F_{1y} \\ F_{2x} \\ F_{2y} \end{Bmatrix} = \frac{AE}{L} \begin{bmatrix} \cos^2\theta & \cos\theta\sin\theta & -\cos^2\theta & -\cos\theta\sin\theta \\ \cos\theta\sin\theta & \sin^2\theta & -\cos\theta\sin\theta & -\sin^2\theta \\ -\cos^2\theta & -\cos\theta\sin\theta & \cos^2\theta & \cos\theta\sin\theta \\ -\cos\theta\sin\theta & -\sin^2\theta & \cos\theta\sin\theta & \sin^2\theta \end{bmatrix} \begin{Bmatrix} u_{1x} \\ u_{1y} \\ u_{2x} \\ u_{2y} \end{Bmatrix} \tag{5.9}$$

Take a moment to compare Equations (5.8b) and (5.9). You can see that moving from a one-dimensional analysis to a two-dimensional analysis has doubled the size of the force and displacement vectors, and quadrupled the size of the stiffness matrix. (Don't worry, I won't be troubling you with any three-dimensional analysis of this type!)

Although I don't want to carry the computation through in full, I still want to talk you through the analysis a little further. Hopefully, you will continue to see the parallels with the one-dimensional case, and also appreciate the degree of complexity that necessitates the use of a computer for this type of analysis.

To solve for the forces and displacements at the nodes in the three-element PJS of Figure 5.55 it is necessary to formulate a *local* stiffness matrix for each element and then assemble a *global* stiffness matrix for the structure as a whole, just as we did for our one-dimensional model.

For element (1), which links nodes 1 and 2, we have $\theta = 60°$. Hence, $\cos \theta = 1/2$ and $\sin \theta = \sqrt{3}/2$. So the stiffness matrix for this element is:

$$
k^{(1)} = \frac{AE}{L}
\begin{array}{c}
\begin{matrix} u_{1x} & u_{1y} & u_{2x} & u_{2y} \end{matrix} \\
\left[
\begin{matrix}
\dfrac{1}{4} & \dfrac{\sqrt{3}}{4} & -\dfrac{1}{4} & -\dfrac{\sqrt{3}}{4} \\[8pt]
\dfrac{\sqrt{3}}{4} & \dfrac{3}{4} & -\dfrac{\sqrt{3}}{4} & -\dfrac{3}{4} \\[8pt]
-\dfrac{1}{4} & -\dfrac{\sqrt{3}}{4} & \dfrac{1}{4} & \dfrac{\sqrt{3}}{4} \\[8pt]
-\dfrac{\sqrt{3}}{4} & -\dfrac{3}{4} & \dfrac{\sqrt{3}}{4} & \dfrac{3}{4}
\end{matrix}
\right]
\begin{matrix} u_{1x} \\[8pt] u_{1y} \\[8pt] u_{2x} \\[8pt] u_{2y} \end{matrix}
\end{array}
$$

For element (2), which links nodes 2 and 3, $\theta = 120°$. Hence, $\cos \theta = -1/2$ and $\sin \theta = \sqrt{3}/2$, so:

$$
k^{(2)} = \frac{AE}{L}
\begin{array}{c}
\begin{matrix} u_{2x} & u_{2y} & u_{3x} & u_{3y} \end{matrix} \\
\left[
\begin{matrix}
\dfrac{1}{4} & -\dfrac{\sqrt{3}}{4} & -\dfrac{1}{4} & \dfrac{\sqrt{3}}{4} \\[8pt]
-\dfrac{\sqrt{3}}{4} & \dfrac{3}{4} & \dfrac{\sqrt{3}}{4} & -\dfrac{3}{4} \\[8pt]
-\dfrac{1}{4} & \dfrac{\sqrt{3}}{4} & \dfrac{1}{4} & -\dfrac{\sqrt{3}}{4} \\[8pt]
\dfrac{\sqrt{3}}{4} & -\dfrac{3}{4} & -\dfrac{\sqrt{3}}{4} & \dfrac{3}{4}
\end{matrix}
\right]
\begin{matrix} u_{2x} \\[8pt] u_{2y} \\[8pt] u_{3x} \\[8pt] u_{3y} \end{matrix}
\end{array}
$$

Finally, for element (3), which links nodes 3 and 1, $\theta = 0°$. Hence, $\cos \theta = 1$ and $\sin \theta = 0$, so this matrix looks a lot sparser:

$$
k^{(3)} = \frac{AE}{L}
\begin{array}{c}
\begin{matrix} u_{3x} & u_{3y} & u_{1x} & u_{1y} \end{matrix} \\
\left[
\begin{matrix}
1 & 0 & -1 & 0 \\[8pt]
0 & 0 & 0 & 0 \\[8pt]
-1 & 0 & 1 & 0 \\[8pt]
0 & 0 & 0 & 0
\end{matrix}
\right]
\begin{matrix} u_{3x} \\[8pt] u_{3y} \\[8pt] u_{1x} \\[8pt] u_{1y} \end{matrix}
\end{array}
$$

These three local stiffness matrices contain information about two nodes each. They can be combined into a single global stiffness matrix that contains information about all three nodes, and then assembled into an equation of the form of Equations (5.8a), (5.8b) and (5.9), thus:

$$
\begin{Bmatrix} F_{1x} \\ F_{1y} \\ F_{2x} \\ F_{2y} \\ F_{3x} \\ F_{3y} \end{Bmatrix} = \frac{AE}{L}
\begin{bmatrix}
\frac{5}{4} & \frac{\sqrt{3}}{4} & -\frac{1}{4} & -\frac{\sqrt{3}}{4} & -1 & 0 \\[6pt]
\frac{\sqrt{3}}{4} & \frac{3}{4} & -\frac{\sqrt{3}}{4} & -\frac{3}{4} & 0 & 0 \\[6pt]
-\frac{1}{4} & -\frac{\sqrt{3}}{4} & \frac{1}{2} & 0 & -\frac{1}{4} & \frac{\sqrt{3}}{4} \\[6pt]
-\frac{\sqrt{3}}{4} & -\frac{3}{4} & 0 & \frac{6}{4} & \frac{\sqrt{3}}{4} & -\frac{3}{4} \\[6pt]
-1 & 0 & -\frac{1}{4} & \frac{\sqrt{3}}{4} & \frac{5}{4} & -\frac{\sqrt{3}}{4} \\[6pt]
0 & 0 & \frac{\sqrt{3}}{4} & -\frac{3}{4} & -\frac{\sqrt{3}}{4} & \frac{3}{4}
\end{bmatrix}
\begin{Bmatrix} u_{1x} \\ u_{1y} \\ u_{2x} \\ u_{2y} \\ u_{3x} \\ u_{3y} \end{Bmatrix}
$$

Note that the global stiffness matrix in Equation (5.10) links six forces to six displacements, and is created by summing all the contributions from the local stiffness matrices. For example, the value at the (u_{1x}, u_{1x}) position in $k^{(1)}$ is 1/4, and in $k^{(3)}$ that value is 1; there is no (u_{1x}, u_{1x}) position in the $k^{(2)}$ matrix, since element 2 is not linked to node 1. In Equation (5.10), the value at the (u_{1x}, u_{1x}) position in the global stiffness matrix is 5/4, i.e. the sum of 1/4 and 1.

Assuming that we know the geometries and elastic moduli of the bars from which our truss is constructed, Equation (5.10) represents six simultaneous equations with 12 'unknown' forces and displacements. That's too many to come to a solution – there needs to be one unknown per equation. But we can easily fix that.

EXERCISE 5.7

By referring to the model truss in Figure 5.55, assign values (including 'zero' where appropriate) to as many of the six forces (F_{1x}, F_{1y}, etc.) and six displacements (u_{1x}, u_{1y}, etc.) as you can. These are the model boundary conditions. (Assume forces acting in the positive x- or y-directions are positive and those acting in the negative x- or y-directions are negative.)

Applying the boundary conditions you determined in Exercise 5.7, Equation (5.10) can be rewritten as:

$$\left\{\begin{array}{c} F_{1x} \\ F_{1y} \\ 1414 \\ -1414 \\ F_{3x} \\ F_{3y} \end{array}\right\} = \frac{AE}{L} \begin{array}{cccccc} u_{1x} & u_{1y} & u_{2x} & u_{2y} & u_{3x} & u_{3y} \\ \begin{bmatrix} \dfrac{5}{4} & \dfrac{\sqrt{3}}{4} & -\dfrac{1}{4} & -\dfrac{\sqrt{3}}{4} & -1 & 0 \\[2mm] \dfrac{\sqrt{3}}{4} & \dfrac{3}{4} & -\dfrac{\sqrt{3}}{4} & -\dfrac{3}{4} & 0 & 0 \\[2mm] -\dfrac{1}{4} & -\dfrac{\sqrt{3}}{4} & \dfrac{1}{2} & 0 & -\dfrac{1}{4} & \dfrac{\sqrt{3}}{4} \\[2mm] -\dfrac{\sqrt{3}}{4} & -\dfrac{3}{4} & 0 & \dfrac{6}{4} & \dfrac{\sqrt{3}}{4} & -\dfrac{3}{4} \\[2mm] -1 & 0 & -\dfrac{1}{4} & \dfrac{\sqrt{3}}{4} & \dfrac{5}{4} & -\dfrac{\sqrt{3}}{4} \\[2mm] 0 & 0 & \dfrac{\sqrt{3}}{4} & -\dfrac{3}{4} & -\dfrac{\sqrt{3}}{4} & \dfrac{3}{4} \end{bmatrix} \end{array} \left\{\begin{array}{c} 0 \\ 0 \\ u_{2x} \\ u_{2y} \\ 0 \\ 0 \end{array}\right\} \quad (5.11)$$

which now represents six simultaneous equations with six unknowns. Note that the unknown nodal forces in this analysis, F_{1x}, F_{1y}, etc., are the *reaction* forces at the pinned nodes. For a structure made of 1 m long steel bars of cross-sectional area 500 mm^2, with $E = 200$ GPa (so that $AE/L = 10^8$ N m^{-1}), the above matrix, Equation (5.11), can be solved computationally with the following result:

$$F_{1x} = -0.299 \text{ kN}$$
$$F_{1y} = -0.518 \text{ kN}$$
$$F_{3x} = -1.115 \text{ kN}$$
$$F_{3y} = 1.932 \text{ kN}$$
$$u_{2x} = -2.828 \times 10^{-5} \text{ m}$$
$$u_{2y} = -9.427 \times 10^{-6} \text{ m}$$

I can't really 'prove' to you that those answers are right, but you can at least check that the forces balance by considering equilibrium in the *x*- and *y*-directions.

EXERCISE 5.8

If the truss structure of Figure 5.55 is in equilibrium, the sum of all the nodal forces in the *x*- and *y*-directions should balance. Check that this is so, using the boundary conditions and the given solution to Equation (5.11).

Obviously, once we have obtained all the reaction forces at the supports, we can employ the usual equilibrium equations at the joints (i.e. the method of joints) to determine the internal forces in the members.

Software using the stiffness matrix method provides a very powerful method of analysing truss structures. Furthermore, although it looks daunting on paper, the mathematics are not actually that computationally demanding and so can be run on personal computers. Obviously, there are large numbers of structures that cannot be well modelled as trusses. These must be treated as continuum structures, where it is assumed that they are subjected to stress in at least two, and possibly three, dimensions. The standard way of analysing these structures is to represent the continuum body as a mesh of discrete elements joined together at nodes. You have already seen several examples of this: the tie bar and crane hook we looked at in Parts 1 and 2, for example.

It is important to carry out specific checks on both the input data and the results of any finite element model, and validation with experimental measurements should be seriously considered where the results are particularly influential to any design or structural integrity decision.

The following lists are not exhaustive and are used to illustrate the kinds of *reality* check that should be applied to finite element calculations.

Checks on input data and model include ensuring that:

- the geometry of the structure is suitably modelled and meshed

- the boundary conditions are reasonable

- the direction and magnitude of the loads have been correctly specified

- the correct material properties are being used.

Checks on output data include ensuring that:

- the applied loads and support reactions are in equilibrium

- the directions and relative magnitudes of the deformations are reasonable

- the displacements and loads are of the right order of magnitude.

Note that to check the quality of the output you need to have a rough idea of what is a reasonable solution to your problem. This is why a fundamental understanding of the underlying principles of structural analysis and an ability to produce 'order of magnitude' estimates of the loads on structures is essential even today, when so many computer programs are available to help us. Otherwise, as described in ⊠ **A cautionary tale** ⊠, disaster can result.

▽ A cautionary tale

A spectacular recent example of the limitations of computer analysis and design methods was the loss of the Sleipner, an offshore oil platform in the Norwegian sector of the North Sea. This enormous concrete structure, over 100 m high (comparable to a 30-storey building), took three years to design and construct. During installation in 1991, a shear failure in the wall of one of the huge hollow cells that made up the base initiated a catastrophic collapse, causing an estimated economic loss of US$700 million.

The structure had been analysed and designed using sophisticated computer software, which first performed a global finite element analysis of the structure and then carried out detailed strength checks at several thousand locations under several hundred different load cases. Unfortunately, because of quite small errors in the assumptions made in both the global analysis and the strength calculations, the wall that failed was not identified as a critical location and so was not checked!

Faced with enormous financial pressure to build a replacement, and the obvious need for a major revision to their computer software, the engineers took the decision to design the new structure using simple hand calculations. By the time the new computer results were available, the design was complete and most of the structure had been built. It has now been operating safely for several years.

The lesson is obvious; no matter how large and complex the structure, or how sophisticated the computer software available, it is *always* possible to obtain the most important design parameters from relatively simple hand calculations. Such calculations should always be performed, both as a check on computer output and to improve the engineer's understanding of the structural behaviour.

(Source: Williams and Todd (2000), *Structures*, p. 312)

7 CASE STUDY 2: FAILURE ANALYSIS OF A CONCRETE SPRAYER

We saw earlier that all structural and stress analyses are models of reality. They may differ in their realism and potential accuracy, but none is a perfect description, and thus an element of uncertainty is included in any analysis. We overcome this problem when designing structures by making sure any design is conservative. Similarly, when we perform a structural analysis on a structure or device that already exists, we must be aware of the limitations of the model we use to calculate loads and stresses. However, even calculations using relatively simplistic models can actually be very useful, as I hope the following case study will show.

7.1 Background

This case study concerns the alleged unexpected failure of a pressurized cement pump while in service. The cement pump failed when the lid of the machine sprung open while under pressure, causing injury to its operator. The calculations described here were performed as part of an investigation into the cause of the failure.

Basically, the machine comprises a chamber in which water and grout cement are stirred by a paddle, driven by a motor. Once the correct mix has been achieved, the chamber is pressurized to 100 psi (0.69 MPa) and the mix is then delivered to its destination by hose. A general view of the top half of the device is shown in Figure 5.57.

To pressurize the chamber, the operator first closes the lid by closing down a box-section lever (lever A in Figure 5.58) that is attached to the lid. The box section

Figure 5.57 Top of cement pump

Figure 5.58 Cement-pump clamp geometry

is then secured by bringing down a cam-lever arrangement (lever B in Figure 5.58), hinged at the opposite end of the pressure chamber, to the box lever. The cam-lever arm drops between a pair of lugs and a securing cotter pin is used to restrain it. When the chamber is under pressure, the force on the chamber lid reacted through the lever arrangement is sufficient to hold the arm in place. This arrangement can be most easily understood by inspection of Figure 5.59, which is a photograph of the relevant area on the cement pump.

Figure 5.59 Details of the camlock arrangement

If you look for the worn contact areas on the cams (the small round protuberances) on both the box and the cam levers you can see that, when they engage, the box lever is fixed in place by a force that is transmitted through both cams. If you now go back and study Figure 5.57 you will see that this force is reacted by the pin and clevis arrangement that holds the cam lever down, which is located just above the box lever hinge. The clevis comprises a pair of lugs welded onto the box section.

The purpose of this arrangement is to create a big mechanical advantage in a relatively small physical space, i.e. it allows a relatively small force to rotate the cam lever through a large angle, creating a larger force at the cams that pushes the lid firmly onto the chamber.

One of the questions that had to be addressed during the investigation was: 'When the pump is operating, is the force exerted by the cam lever on the cotter pin sufficient to cause the welds securing the lugs to the box lever to fail?'

7.2 Structural analysis

To answer this question, a structural analysis must be performed on the system to estimate the forces that might be imposed on both the cotter pin and the lug welds when the pump is pressurized to its normal operating value. The box-section arm, a failed lug and the original cotter pin were available and were measured to enable estimates of the dimensions of the critical parts and the angles that the various levers adopt in normal operation to be obtained; and these, alone, are actually sufficient to calculate the loads on the cotter pin and weld lug.

Of course, as we noted above, it is impossible to calculate the exact forces involved, owing to uncertainties in the exact geometry of the system at the time of failure, as well as difficulties in estimating other factors such as the frictional forces involved; but useful estimates can be obtained.

When operated normally at its specified pressure, the force on the pump lid is significant. However, the load path is designed so that the major part of this is reacted through the camlock. Indeed, if the cam in the camlock were operated so that the contact force were vertical, then the force on the camlock lever itself would be negligible.

However, it is clear from Figure 5.58 that in operation the cam acts at a significant angle from the vertical, and thus the force acting through the lever onto the cotter pin will be finite. Indeed, careful measurements showed that the cam lever makes an angle of ~27° to the horizontal, which means the cam makes an angle of ~63° to the vertical in normal operation.

From these measurements, a sketch of the main components and the forces acting on them can be drawn, as shown in Figure 5.60.

SAQ 5.12 (Learning outcome 5.3)

Draw FBDs of (a) the box lever A and (b) the cam lever B, and hence identify the forces that act on each.

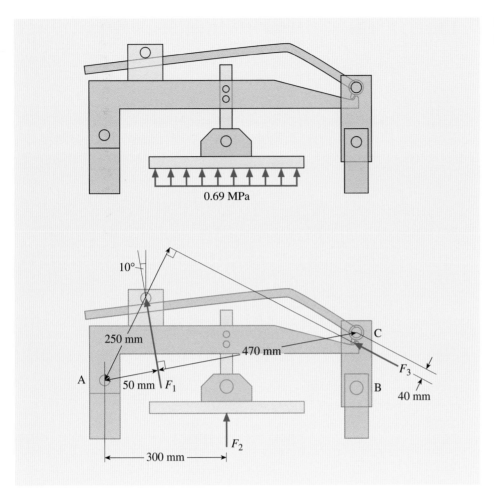

Figure 5.60   Lever arrangement

The forces identified in the SAQ are as follows.

F_1 is the force exerted by the cam lever on the cotter pin. This is the force we want to estimate.

F_2 is the force exerted by the lid on the pressure pan on the box lever. This large force is the force that is reacted by the lever arrangement.

F_3 is the force exerted by the box cam on the cam lever.

R_{Ax} and R_{Ay} are the horizontal and vertical components of the force exerted at the pin-joint hinge (point A) of the box lever.

R_{Cx} and R_{Cy} are the horizontal and vertical components of the force exerted at the pin-joint hinge (point C) of the cam lever.

We can calculate F_2 from the area of the pump lid and the pressure that it is subjected to. Given F_2, what we need to do is estimate the sizes of F_1 and F_3.

We are not interested in calculating the forces at the pin joints. Thus, for each lever we can take moments at the pin joint to gain information about the forces F_1 and F_3.

We also need the geometry of the device: the angles and dimensions are shown in Figure 5.61.

Figure 5.61   Sketch of lever arrangement showing forces acting and geometry

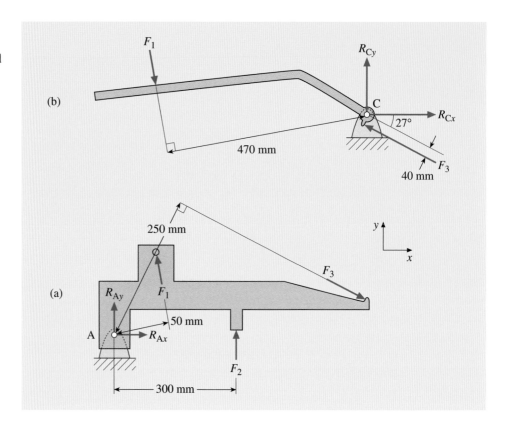

Now, F_2 is just the product of the lid area times the pressure it is subjected to. The lid is 250 mm in diameter and subjected to a pressure of 0.69 MPa.

So the force is:

$$F_2 = \text{pressure} \times \text{area} = 689 \times 10^3 \text{ N m}^{-2} \times \frac{\pi \times 250^2}{4} \times 10^{-6} \text{ m}^2 = 33.9 \text{ kN}$$

So the force that the lid has to resist is 33.9 kN. This is a significant force, equivalent to the force exerted by a mass of approximately 3.4 tonnes.

SAQ 5.13 (Learning outcomes 5.3 and 5.4)

Using the information provided, estimate the force F_1 that acts on the cam lever when the pump is pressurized.

Hint: you will probably want to take moments about points A and C.

We now need to compare this value of 3.5 kN for F_1 with the force that we predict would cause the lug welds to fail. In the actual investigation, a conservative approach was taken. Although including frictional forces would be more likely to decrease than increase the estimate of F_1, the calculated value was increased to 5 kN when considering its implications.

So, even allowing for the assumptions in this calculation, we can safely assume that the force the cam lever imparts to the cotter pin will not be more than 5 kN (i.e. equivalent to the force exerted by a mass of about 0.5 tonnes). Now, this will be reacted by the two lugs securing the cotter pin that holds the cam lever, so the force in each lug will be about 2.5 kN.

SAQ 5.14 (Learning outcomes 5.1 and Block 1 revision)

(a) The lugs are welded onto the lid-retaining arm, with an attachment area of about 500 mm². Calculate the stress in the lug arising from the force of 2.5 kN.

(b) Inspection of the lug shows that it was only tack welded to the arm. Calculate the stress again, assuming that only 10% of the weld was good, so that we have a useful weld area of only 50 mm².

(c) A poor weld might have a failure stress as low as 250 MPa. What area of weld would give this stress with a force of 2.5 kN?

The SAQ shows that we would have to assume that only 2% of the weld is effective before the stress on the joint reaches 250 MPa. This seems unreasonably low, and indeed examination of the lug that failed (Figure 5.62) showed that the area of good weld is significantly larger than this, so it was concluded extremely unlikely that the lug could have failed during the normal operation of the cam lever.

Figure 5.62 Fracture surface of welded lug

10 mm

(a)

weld

lug

(b)

Just pause for a moment to consider what we have achieved here. By looking only at the geometry of the cement pump, and knowing its operating pressure, we have managed to estimate the forces at key points in its structure, and shown that these forces would not have caused failure in normal operation if the pump housing was properly constructed. So whatever did happen, it wasn't because of a fundamental flaw in the design.

7.3 Conclusion?

The real reason for the pump failure, therefore, cannot be calculated simply by looking at the forces involved. Examination of other parts of the failed vessel showed signs of impact damage, and the failure may, therefore, have been caused because the pump was being operated without the damage having been repaired properly.

What this case study shows is that structural analysis can be useful even if very simple models are used. The important thing is always to be aware of the simplifications and assumptions inherent in the model and to realize that even the most sophisticated, modern, full-scale numerical simulation is still a model of reality.

8 SUMMARY

This part of Block 1 has introduced you to some of the tools for the analysis of structures, which has extended the concepts from earlier in the course where we were looking at single components or elements of a structure. The final case study is a good example of how knowledge of the geometry of a problem and the loads applied to it can allow quite detailed calculation of the stresses in all parts of a structure.

In this part we have kept to fairly simple, idealized structures, whose members are subjected to axial forces only. Simplifying assumptions, such as the concept of the pin joint, make it possible to find the solution to problems that might otherwise be insoluble by straightforward analysis of the type we have used here.

In practice, though, idealized pin-jointed structures rarely exist. Most structures are subjected to more complicated loads, and real joints tend to be rigid. So, in the next part, I will extend the types of analysis so that we can start building up techniques that can tackle more realistic structures. We will look at the response of structural members subjected to more complicated loads, namely bending and torsion. We will also look at a common stability issue in structures: *buckling*.

LEARNING OUTCOMES

After studying Block 1 Part 5 you should be able to do the following.

5.1 Describe qualitatively the likely stress state in a structure or part of a structure.

5.2 Idealize a structure as a simple two-dimensional PJS, making simplifications where appropriate.

5.3 Calculate the forces in members of simple structures using equilibrium of forces and moments of forces.

5.4 Use the method of joints and/or the method of sections, as appropriate, to calculate the internal forces in simple structures.

5.5 Assess whether or not a structure is statically determinate, statically indeterminate, or a mechanism.

5.6 Suggest ways in which a structure can be made statically determinate by the addition or removal of members.

ANSWERS TO EXERCISES

EXERCISE 5.1

It is assumed that the load is applied at the centre of the cable. So, the FBD of the part of the cable where the load F is applied can be drawn as shown in Figure 5.63.

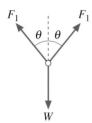

Figure 5.63   Free-body diagram of cable with a single point load

Applying vertical equilibrium:

$$\sum F_y = 0$$
$$2\left(F_1 \cos \theta\right) - W = 0$$

Therefore:

$$F_1 = \frac{W}{2\cos\theta}$$

So:

for $\theta = 45°$, $F_1 = 0.7W$

for $\theta = 60°$, $F_1 = 1.0W$

for $\theta = 75°$, $F_1 = 1.9W$.

That is, the larger the sag is (i.e. the smaller the angle θ), the lower the tension in the cable will be.

EXERCISE 5.2

The free-body diagrams of the eyebolts at A and B are shown in Figure 5.64.

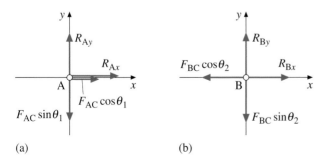

(a)   (b)

Figure 5.64   Free-body diagrams of the eyebolts at points A and B

We can find the reaction forces by equilibrating the forces in each FBD. Starting with eyebolt A (Figure 5.64a):

$$\sum F_y = 0$$
$$-F_{AC} \sin \theta_1 + R_{Ay} = 0$$

Therefore:

$$R_{Ay} = 849.6 \text{ N} \times \sin 60° = 735.8 \text{ N}$$

And:

$$\sum F_x = 0$$
$$F_{AC} \cos \theta_1 + R_{Ax} = 0$$

Therefore:

$$R_{Ax} = -849.6 \text{ N} \times \cos 60° = -424.8 \text{ N}$$

Equilibrating forces in the FBD of eyebolt B (Figure 5.64b) in the y-direction gives:

$$\sum F_y = 0$$
$$-F_{BC} \sin \theta_2 + R_{By} = 0$$

Thus:

$$R_{By} = 490.5 \text{ N} \times \sin 30° = 245.3 \text{ N}$$

And in the x-direction:

$$\sum F_x = 0$$
$$-F_{BC} \cos \theta_2 + R_{Bx} = 0$$

Thus:

$$R_{Bx} = 490.5 \text{ N} \times \cos 30° = 424.8 \text{ N}$$

So, taking the whole system as an FBD, the reaction forces should balance the weight of the crate. That is, the summation of the vertical reaction forces:

$$R_{Ay} + R_{By} = 735.8 \text{ N} + 245.3 \text{ N} = 981.1 \text{ N}$$

which corresponds to the weight of a crate of mass 100 kg (with a small rounding error).

Since there is no load applied in the horizontal direction, the sum of the forces R_{Ax} and R_{Bx} is zero.

EXERCISE 5.3

(a) The wing of an aircraft is essentially a beam.

(b) The roof of a car is either a plate or a shell, depending on the curvature.

(c) A concrete bridge like the one shown in Figure 5.18 is essentially a beam.

EXERCISE 5.4

Taking $x'y'$ as the reference frame (Figure 5.34), the equilibrium of forces in the y'-direction gives:

$$\sum F_{y'} = 0$$
$$F_A \sin 15° - F_{AB} \cos 30° = 0$$

Therefore:

$$F_{AB} = F_A \frac{\sin 15°}{\cos 30°}$$
$$= 2 \text{ kN} \times \frac{\sin 15°}{\cos 30°}$$
$$= 0.60 \text{ kN}$$

Equilibrium of forces in the x'-direction gives:

$$\sum F_{x'} = 0$$
$$F_A \cos 15° + F_{AB} \sin 30° + F_{AC} = 0$$

Therefore:

$$F_{AC} = -F_{AB} \sin 30° - F_A \cos 15°$$
$$= -2.23 \text{ kN}$$

which agrees with the previous calculations.

EXERCISE 5.5

The section of the Warren truss is shown in Figure 5.65.

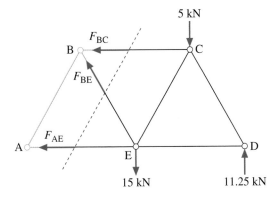

Figure 5.65   Section of the Warren truss in Figure 5.44

The lines of action for both F_{AE} and F_{BE} go through, naturally, the point where the members join, i.e. pin E. So, taking moments about E eliminates these two forces from the equilibrium equation, leaving only one unknown force, F_{BC}:

$$\sum M_E = 0$$
$$(F_{BC} \times 0.866 \text{ m}) - (5 \text{ kN} \times 0.5 \text{ m}) + (11.25 \text{ kN} \times 1 \text{ m}) = 0$$

Therefore:

$$F_{BC} = -\frac{11.25 \text{ kN m} - 2.5 \text{ kN m}}{0.866 \text{ m}} = -10.10 \text{ kN}$$

EXERCISE 5.6

The force in ram CD, F_{CD}, can be calculated by taking moments about pin joint E. First, the moment arms of the forces need to be determined. In Figure 5.54, the distance L_{DE} between pivot E and pivot D, where the force F_{CD} is applied, is found by the trigonometric relation:

$$L_{DE} = \frac{1.5 \text{ m}}{\cos 20°} = 1.6 \text{ m}$$

For L_{DE} to be the moment arm, we need to take the perpendicular component of the force F_{CD} to the distance L_{DE}. The angle between the line of action of the force F_{CD} and the normal to the line L_{DE} is found as $37° - 20° = 17°$, so the normal component is $F_{CD} \cos 17°$.

The moment arm for the 20 kN force is 4 m, since this is the shortest distance between pivot E and the line of action of the force. F_{CD} can now be calculated by taking moments about pin joint E:

$$\sum M_E = 0$$
$$-(F_{CD} \cos 17° \times 1.6 \text{ m}) - (20 \text{ kN} \times 4 \text{ m}) = 0$$

Therefore:

$$F_{CD} = -52.3 \text{ kN}$$

That is, the ram CD applies a compressive force of 52.3 kN at D.

EXERCISE 5.7

Nodes 1 and 3 are pinned, so the displacements here are all zero, i.e.:

$$u_{1x} = u_{1y} = u_{3x} = u_{3y} = 0$$

The magnitude of force in both the x- and y-directions at node 2 is $(2 \text{ kN} \times \cos 45°) = 1.414 \text{ kN}$. The x-direction force acts to the right and is positive, and the y-direction force acts downwards and is negative, thus:

$$F_{2x} = 1.414 \text{ kN}$$

and

$$F_{2y} = -1.414 \text{ kN}$$

EXERCISE 5.8

Total forces in the x-direction:

$$F_{1x} + F_{2x} + F_{3x} = -0.299 \text{ kN} + 1.414 \text{ kN} - 1.115 \text{ kN} = 0$$

Total forces in the y-direction:

$$F_{1y} + F_{2y} + F_{3y} = -0.518 \text{ kN} - 1.414 \text{ kN} + 1.932 \text{ kN} = 0$$

The principle of force equilibrium is obeyed.

ANSWERS TO SELF-ASSESSMENT QUESTIONS

SAQ 5.1

(a) The cable would be in tension. Cables cannot carry compressive loads as they do not have compressive rigidity.

(b) A lintel above a doorway acts as a beam in bending, with the weight of the bricks above providing the load, so there will be a tensile stress on the bottom of the beam and a compressive stress on the top surface.

(c) The dome will be compressed by the air pressure outside.

SAQ 5.2

(a)

(b)

Figure 5.66   (a) PJS and (b) free-body diagram of the truss bridge in Figure 5.30

SAQ 5.3

(a) Members AB and BC are in tension; member AC is in compression.

(b) By Newton's Third Law they are equal and opposite to the forces on the PJS. At B, 0.52 kN acting upwards and 1.41 kN acting to the right; at C, 1.93 kN acting downwards.

(c) Neglecting the truss weight, the total force must be the one that was applied to the truss. The y-component of the applied force should balance with the summation of the y-components of the reaction forces and similarly for the x-components.

SAQ 5.4

Taking moments about point C should give the same result:

$$\sum M_C = 0$$
$$-\left(F_A \cos 75° \times 1 \text{ m}\right) - \left(R_{By} \times 1 \text{ m}\right) = 0$$

Therefore:

$$R_{By} = -2 \text{ kN} \times \cos 75° = -0.52 \text{ kN}$$

SAQ 5.5

Consider first the FBD of the whole structure, as shown in Figure 5.67.

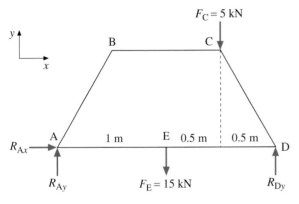

Figure 5.67   Free-body diagram of the whole truss

Applying translational equilibrium:

$$\sum F_x = 0$$
$$R_{Ax} = 0$$

$$\sum F_y = 0$$
$$R_{Ay} + R_{Dy} = 15 \text{ kN} + 5 \text{ kN} \tag{5.12}$$

There are two unknowns, so I need to use moment equilibrium:

$$\sum M_A = 0$$
$$-(15 \text{ kN} \times 1 \text{ m}) - (5 \text{ kN} \times 1.5 \text{ m}) + (R_{Dy} \times 2 \text{ m}) = 0$$

Thus:

$$R_{Dy} = \frac{22.5 \text{ kN m}}{2 \text{ m}} = 11.25 \text{ kN}$$

Therefore, from Equation (5.12):

$$R_{Ay} = 20 \text{ kN} - R_{Dy} = 20 \text{ kN} - 11.25 \text{ kN} = 8.75 \text{ kN}$$

Now I will use the method of joints to consider each pin.

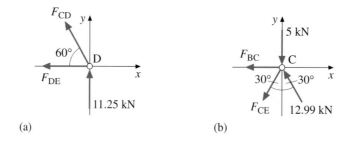

(a)   (b)

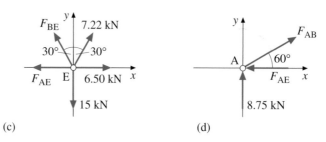

(c)   (d)

Figure 5.68   Free-body diagrams of pins D, C, E and A of Figure 5.40

At pin D (Figure 5.68a):

$$\sum F_y = 0$$
$$F_{CD} \sin 60° + 11.25 \text{ kN} = 0$$

Therefore:

$$F_{CD} = -\frac{11.25 \text{ kN}}{\sin 60°} = -12.99 \text{ kN}$$

$$\sum F_x = 0$$
$$-F_{DE} - F_{CD} \cos 60° = 0$$

So:

$$F_{DE} = -F_{CD} \cos 60° = 6.50 \text{ kN}$$

At pin C (Figure 5.68b), in the y-direction:

$$\sum F_y = 0$$
$$12.99 \text{ kN} \times \cos 30° - F_{CE} \cos 30° - 5 \text{ kN} = 0$$

Thus:

$$F_{CE} = \frac{(12.99 \text{ kN} \times \cos 30°) - 5 \text{ kN}}{\cos 30°} = 7.22 \text{ kN}$$

And in the x-direction:

$$\sum F_x = 0$$
$$-7.22 \text{ kN} \times \cos 60° - 12.99 \text{ kN} \times \cos 60° - F_{BC} = 0$$

Therefore:

$$F_{BC} = -10.11 \text{ kN}$$

At pin E (Figure 5.68c), in the y-direction:

$$\sum F_y = 0$$
$$F_{BE} \cos 30° + 7.22 \text{ kN} \times \cos 30° - 15 \text{ kN} = 0$$

Therefore:

$$F_{BE} = 10.10 \text{ kN}$$

And in the x-direction:

$$\sum F_x = 0$$
$$+F_{AE} - 10.10 \text{ kN} \times \cos 60° + 7.22 \text{ kN} \times \cos 60° + 6.50 \text{ kN} = 0$$

Therefore:

$$F_{AE} = +5.06 \text{ kN}$$

At pin A (Figure 5.68d):

$$\sum F_y = 0$$
$$F_{AB} \sin 60° + 8.75 \text{ kN} = 0$$

Therefore:

$$F_{AB} = -10.10 \text{ kN}$$

SAQ 5.6

The free-body diagram of the whole bridge is shown in Figure 5.69. Since there is no horizontal force applied to the bridge, the horizontal reaction force at the pin support is equal to zero, i.e. $R_{Ax} = 0$. To find the vertical reaction force at C, take moments about A:

$$\sum M_A = 0$$
$$-(2 \text{ kN} \times 2 \text{ m} \times \cos 60°) - (8 \text{ kN} \times 2 \text{ m}) - \left[2 \text{ kN} \times (2 \text{ m} + 1 \text{ m}) \right] + \left(R_{Cy} \times 4 \text{ m} \right) = 0$$

Therefore:

$$R_{Cy} = 6 \text{ kN (i.e. upwards)}$$

The force is positive, and therefore the reaction force is acting upwards as I assumed.

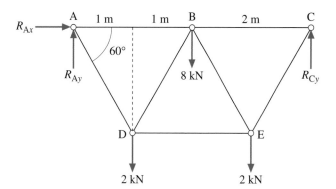

Figure 5.69   Free-body diagram of the bridge structure in Figure 5.41

To find the force in the members, we can use the method of joints. The free-body diagram of pin C (Figure 5.70a) is used to find the force in member BC.

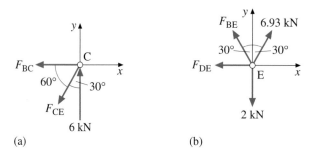

Figure 5.70   Free-body diagrams of pins C and E in the bridge in Figure 5.41

Equilibrium along the y-axis gives:

$$\sum F_y = 0$$
$$6 \text{ kN} - F_{CE} \cos 30° = 0$$

Therefore:

$$F_{CE} = 6.93 \text{ kN}$$

Equilibrium along the x-axis gives:

$$\sum F_x = 0$$
$$-F_{BC} - F_{CE} \sin 30° = 0$$

Thus:

$$F_{BC} = -3.47 \text{ kN}$$

The FBD of pin E (Figure 5.70b) is used to find the force in member BE:

$$\sum F_y = 0$$
$$F_{BE} \cos 30° + 6.93 \text{ kN} \times \cos 30° - 2 \text{ kN} = 0$$

Therefore:

$$F_{BE} = -4.62 \text{ kN}$$

SAQ 5.7

First take the whole truss as a free body, without the internal details; see Figure 5.71.

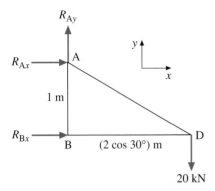

Figure 5.71   Free-body diagram of the whole structure in Figure 5.42

Equilibrium along the y-axis:

$$\sum F_y = 0$$
$$R_{Ay} - 20 \text{ kN} = 0$$

Therefore:

$$R_{Ay} = 20 \text{ kN}$$

Taking moments about B:

$$\sum M_B = 0$$
$$-(R_{Ax} \times 1 \text{ m}) - (20 \text{ kN} \times 2 \text{ m} \times \cos 30°) = 0$$

Therefore:

$$R_{Ax} = -34.64 \text{ kN}$$

Equilibrium along the x-axis:

$$\sum F_x = 0$$
$$R_{Ax} + R_{Bx} = 0$$

Therefore:

$$R_{Bx} = -R_{Ax} = 34.64 \text{ kN}$$

At pin D (Figure 5.72a), along the y-axis:

$$\sum F_y = 0$$
$$F_{CD} \cos 60° - 20 \text{ kN} = 0$$

Therefore:

$$F_{CD} = 40 \text{ kN}$$

Member CD is in 40 kN tension.

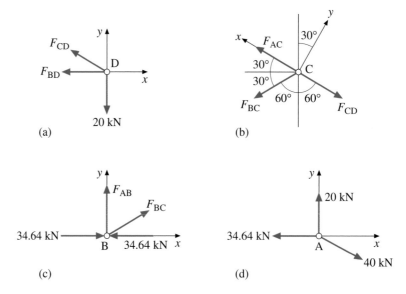

Figure 5.72   Free-body diagram of each pin in Figure 5.42

At pin D, along the x-axis:

$$\sum F_x = 0$$
$$-F_{BD} - F_{CD}\cos 30° = 0$$

Therefore:

$$F_{BD} = -34.64 \text{ kN}$$

Member BD is in 34.64 kN compression.

At pin C (Figure 5.72b), along the y-axis:

$$\sum F_y = 0$$
$$-F_{BC}\cos 30° = 0$$

So $F_{BC} = 0$, i.e. there is no force in member BC.

At pin C, along the x-axis:

$$\sum F_x = 0$$
$$F_{AC} - F_{CD} = 0$$

So:

$$F_{AC} = F_{CD} = 40 \text{ kN}$$

Therefore AC is in 40 kN tension.

At pin B (Figure 5.72c), along the y-axis:

$$\sum F_y = 0$$
$$F_{AB} = 0$$

Therefore there is no force in member AB.

I can check my calculations at pin A (Figure 5.72d).

Along the x-axis:

$$\sum F_x = 0$$
$$40\ \text{kN} \times \cos 30° - 34.64\ \text{kN} = 0$$

which is correct.

Along the y-axis:

$$\sum F_y = 0$$
$$20\ \text{kN} - 40\ \text{kN} \times \cos 60° = 0$$

Note that although some members have zero calculated force, this does not mean that they could be omitted from a real construction. The real force will never be exactly zero.

SAQ 5.8

Figure 5.73 shows the PJS of the roof truss with the dimensions calculated from the given data. First, we need to calculate the reaction forces. We have only a vertical reaction force at B as it is a roller support, and the horizontal reaction at A, $R_{Ax} = 0$ since there are no horizontal forces applied to the structure. We can find the vertical reaction forces by considering the whole truss as a free-body diagram. Taking moments about B gives:

$$\sum M_B = 0$$
$$-\left(R_{Ay} \times 12\ \text{m} \right) + \left(5\ \text{kN} \times 9\ \text{m} \right) + \left(3\ \text{kN} \times 3\ \text{m} \right) = 0$$

So:

$$R_{Ay} = \frac{54\ \text{kN m}}{12\ \text{m}} = 4.5\ \text{kN}$$

Applying equilibrium along the y-axis:

$$\sum F_y = 0$$
$$4.5\ \text{kN} - 5\ \text{kN} - 3\ \text{kN} + R_{By} = 0$$

So:

$$R_{By} = 3.5\ \text{kN}$$

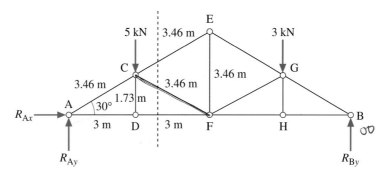

Figure 5.73   Free-body diagram of the roof truss structure in Figure 5.45

We'll use the method of sections first to find the force in member CF.

We make a cut along the dashed line in the PJS of the roof truss (Figure 5.73) to expose the unknown force in member CF. The free-body diagram of the left-hand section, Figure 5.74, shows additional two unknown forces. A careful examination reveals that these two forces, F_{CE} and F_{DF}, which we are not interested in, pass through a common point, A. So, if we take moments about A, then these two unknown forces will not appear in the equation, leaving F_{CF} the only unknown force:

$$\sum M_A$$
$$-(5 \text{ kN} \times 3 \text{ m}) - (F_{CF} \cos 30° \times 3.46 \text{ m}) = 0$$

Therefore:

$$F_{CF} = -\frac{15 \text{ kN m}}{3 \text{ m}} = -5 \text{ kN}$$

Now, employing method of joints to find the same force.

We start from pin A to find the forces in the members, and work our way towards the member CF. (We can't just start from pin C, since that would reveal four unknown forces).

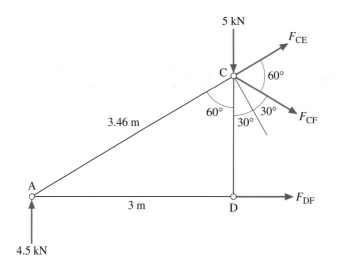

Figure 5.74   Free-body diagram of the left-hand section of Figure 5.73

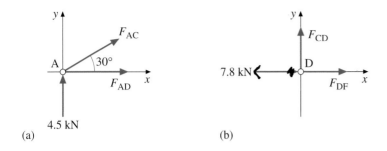

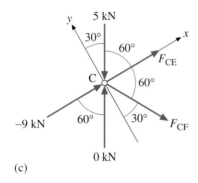

(c)

Figure 5.75   Free-body diagram of pins A, D and C in Figure 5.73

At pin A (Figure 5.75a) there are two unknown forces. Vertical and horizontal equilibrium give:

$$\sum F_y = 0$$
$$4.5 \text{ kN} + F_{AC} \sin 30° = 0$$

So $F_{AC} = -9$ kN.

$$\sum F_x = 0$$
$$F_{AD} + F_{AC} \cos 30° = 0$$

Thus:

$$F_{AD} = +7.8 \text{ kN}$$

At pin D (Figure 5.75b) we have two unknown forces (Note that F_{AD}, which I determined above, is a ~~negative~~ *positive* force, so it acts ~~towards~~ *away from* the pin. ~~Since I have drawn it in the FBD with its correct direction, I omit the negative sign in the drawing).~~

Horizontal equilibrium at pin D (Figure 5.75b) gives:

$$\sum F_x = 0$$
$$-7.8 \text{ kN} + F_{DF} = 0$$

Therefore:

$$F_{DF} = +7.8 \text{ kN}$$

So, the direction of F_{DF} is also ~~towards~~ *away from* the pin D.

There is only one force in the y-direction and therefore:

$$F_{CD} = 0$$

You may wonder whether we need this zero-force member in our structure at all; couldn't we just remove it, as it doesn't seem to be doing anything useful? Yes, in theory it could be removed without affecting the force equilibrium and the determinacy of the structure (assuming that the joint at D is also removed). However, the long member between pins A and F would be prone to buckling instability if the direction of the external loading on the truss were reversed.

It is interesting to note that the member CD does not carry any force. In fact this was to be expected: in a pin-jointed structure, for joints where three members meet, if two of the members are collinear (as are members AD and DF) and there are no external load or reactions at the joint, then the non-collinear member (i.e. member CD) does not bear any force, and it is usually referred to as a 'zero-force member'.

At pin C (Figure 5.75c) there are two unknowns. But, I have aligned my x-axis with the unknown force F_{AC}, so it will not take part in the equilibrium equation along the y-axis:

$$\sum F_y = 0$$
$$-5\ \text{kN} \times \cos 60° - F_{CF} \cos 60° = 0$$

Therefore:

$$F_{CF} = -5\ \text{kN}$$

which is the same as obtained by the method of sections.

SAQ 5.9

We must first find the reaction forces at the supports. Since all the loads acting on the bridge are vertical, there should not be any horizontal reaction forces (Figure 5.76a).

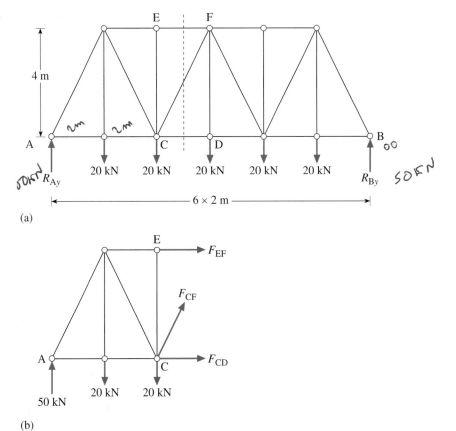

Figure 5.76   (a) PJS and (b) section of the truss bridge in Figure 5.46

Taking moments about A gives:

$$\sum M_A = 0$$
$$-(20 \text{ kN} \times 2 \text{ m}) - (20 \text{ kN} \times 4 \text{ m}) - (20 \text{ kN} \times 6 \text{ m}) - (20 \text{ kN} \times 8 \text{ m}) - (20 \text{ kN} \times 10 \text{ m}) + (R_B \times 12 \text{ m}) = 0$$

So:

$$R_B = 50 \text{ kN}$$

And vertical equilibrium gives:

$$\sum F_y = 0$$
$$R_A + 50 \text{ kN} - (5 \times 20 \text{ kN}) = 0$$

Therefore:

$$R_A = 50 \text{ kN}$$

Of course, we could have found the reaction forces straight away if we had used the symmetrical nature of the bridge and loading; in this case, each support bears half the load.

Next, we make our cut at the members to expose the unknown forces as shown in Figure 5.46 as a dashed line. I have redrawn the left-hand half of the structure in Figure 5.76(b), which I prefer as there are fewer forces involved. There are a few ways of solving for the unknown forces, but they all involve moment equilibrium. Here is one of them: take moments about C, which eliminates F_{CF} and F_{CD} from the equation.

$$\sum M_C = 0$$
$$-(50 \text{ kN} \times 4 \text{ m}) + (20 \text{ kN} \times 2 \text{ m}) - (F_{EF} \times 4 \text{ m}) = 0$$

Therefore:

$$F_{EF} = -40 \text{ kN}$$

Vertical equilibrium gives:

$$\sum F_y = 0$$
$$50 \text{ kN} - 20 \text{ kN} - 20 \text{ kN} + F_{CF} \sin 63° = 0$$

Thus:

$$F_{CF} = -11.22 \text{ kN}$$

Finally, horizontal equilibrium gives:

$$\sum F_x = 0$$
$$-40 \text{ kN} + F_{CD} - 11.22 \text{ kN} \times \cos 63° = 0$$

So:

$$F_{CD} = 45.09 \text{ kN}$$

We could have found the forces by using the method of joints as well. But, this would have been more tedious as we had to go through several joints, starting from one of the supports, and calculate all the forces at each joint.

SAQ 5.10

(a) Applying the determinacy test:

$$m + r - 2j$$

$$9 + 3 - 2 \times 6 = 0$$

So, it appears that this is a statically determinate structure, but a close inspection will reveal that it is in fact not. The upper rectangular element is really a mechanism and the lower element has one redundancy (Figure 5.77a). As there is apparently the correct number of members in the structure (since $m + r - 2j = 0$), moving one of the braces (A or B) from the lower element to the upper element, as shown in Figure 5.77(a), would make the whole structure *truly* statically determinate.

(b) Applying the determinacy test gives: $8 + 3 - 2 \times 6 = -1$. Therefore, this is a mechanism. It is apparent from Figure 5.77(b) which part is causing the problem. The addition of a horizontal member (A) in the middle of the structure would make the structure statically determinate.

(c) The determinacy test gives: $11 + 4 - 2 \times 7 = 1$. Therefore, this is a redundant (or *over-stiff*) structure with one redundancy. It may not be as obvious as the previous examples, but careful examination of the structure should expose the redundancy of the middle roller support (A). Removal of this support would not make the structure collapse, and would make it statically determinate (Figure 5.77c). A second option for making the structure statically determinate is to leave the middle support in place but remove the horizontal member at the top (B). This creates two independent statically determinate structures, using a common support (A).

(d) The determinacy test gives: $14 + 3 - 2 \times 8 = 1$; that is, one redundancy. Again, this is not entirely correct, because the structure has two redundancies and a mechanism at different parts as shown in Figure 5.77(d). Removal of the extra members from the outer rectangular elements and addition of a bracing member in the central element would make the structure statically determinate.

(e) The determinacy test gives: $15 + 3 - 2 \times 8 = 2$; that is, two redundancies. Both rectangular elements are over braced. Removal of one brace from both elements (i.e. A or B, and C or D) would make the structure statically determinate (Figure 5.77e).

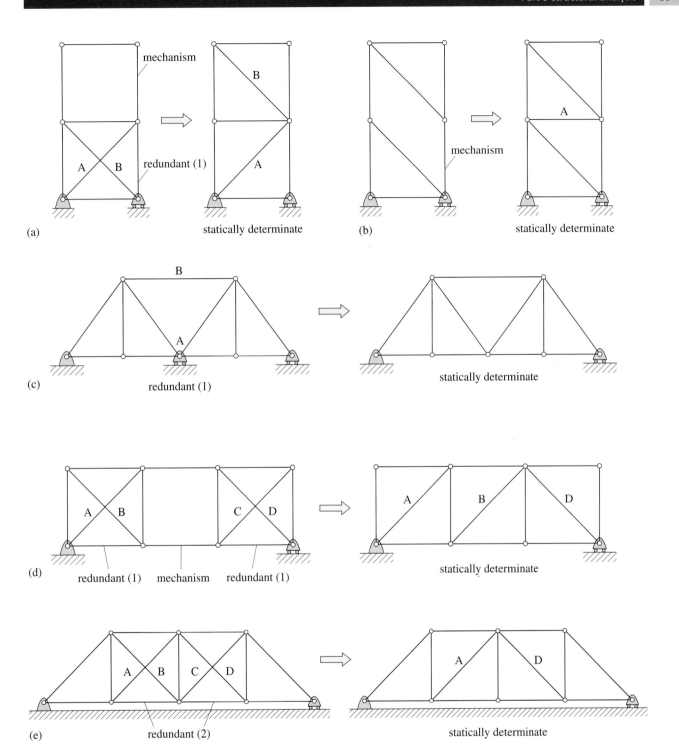

Figure 5.77   Determinacy test of structures in Figure 5.51

SAQ 5.11

To determine the force applied by the ram AC, I have drawn an FBD that combines the arms BE and DH, and the bucket, and the rams CD and FG, as shown in Figure 5.78.

Figure 5.78 Free-body diagram of the arms BE and DH, and the bucket; note that I have not shown the reaction forces at B, for clarity

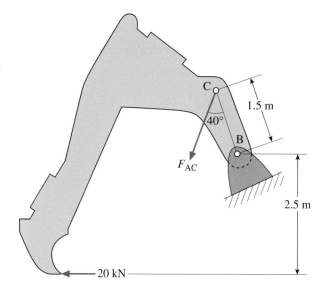

Taking moments about B gives:

$$\sum M_B = 0$$
$$\left(F_{AC}\cos 50° \times 1.5\ \text{m}\right) - \left(20\ \text{kN} \times 2.5\ \text{m}\right) = 0$$

So:

$$F_{AC} = 51.9\ \text{kN}$$

That is, the ram AC applies a tensile force of 51.9 kN at C.

SAQ 5.12

Figure 5.79 Free-body diagrams of (a) the box lever and (b) the cam lever

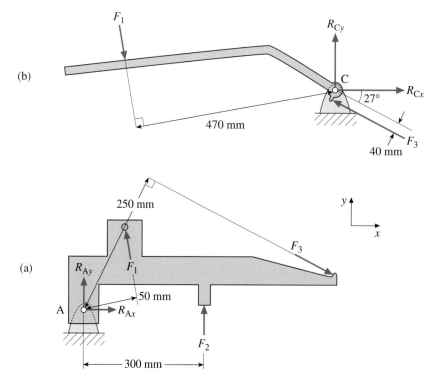

SAQ 5.13

First take moments about point A, the pin joint of the box lever:

$$\sum M_A = 0$$
$$\left(F_1 \times 50 \times 10^{-3}\ \text{m}\right) + \left(F_2 \times 300 \times 10^{-3}\ \text{m}\right) - \left(F_3 \times 250 \times 10^{-3}\ \text{m}\right) = 0$$

This allows us to produce a relationship between F_1 and F_3 thus:

$$\left(F_1 \times 50 \times 10^{-3}\ \text{m}\right) - \left(F_3 \times 250 \times 10^{-3}\ \text{m}\right) = -10\,140\ \text{N m}$$

If we then take moments about point C, the pin joint of the cam lever, we get:

$$\sum M_C = 0$$
$$\left(F_1 \times 470 \times 10^{-3}\ \text{m}\right) - \left(F_3 \times 40 \times 10^{-3}\ \text{m}\right) = 0$$

So:

$$F_3 = \frac{470}{40} F_1 = 11.75 F_1$$

and then substituting this result back in our first equation we find:

$$\left(F_1 \times 50 \times 10^{-3}\ \text{m}\right) - \left(11.75 \times F_1 \times 250 \times 10^{-3}\ \text{m}\right) = -10\,140\ \text{N m}$$

Therefore:

$$F_1 = \frac{10\,140}{2.8875}\ \text{N} = 3512\ \text{N} \approx 3.5\ \text{kN}$$

which is approximately 10% of the force on the pan lid.

SAQ 5.14

(a) The stress would be $2500\ \text{N} \div 5 \times 10^{-4}\ \text{m}^2 = 5\ \text{MPa}$

(b) The stress would be $2500\ \text{N} \div 5 \times 10^{-5}\ \text{m}^2 = 50\ \text{MPa}$

(c) The area would be $250\ \text{MPa} \div 2500\ \text{N} = 1 \times 10^{-5}\ \text{m}^2$

ACKNOWLEDGEMENTS

Grateful acknowledgement is made to the following sources:

FIGURES

Figure 5.2: © David O'Shea/Alamy.

Figure 5.3: © Visions of America. LLC/Alamy.

Figure 5.4: © Aviation Images.

Figure 5.6: © Danita Delimont/Alamy.

Figure 5.7: © Paul Glendell/Alamy.

Figure 5.8: © Robert Estall photo agency/Alamy.

Figure 5.11(e): © Alex Beaton/Alamy.

Figure 5.11(f): © Henry Westheim Photography/Alamy.

Figure 5.18: © Images of France/Alamy.

Figure 5.25(a): © Adrienne Cleveland.

Figure 5.25(b): Courtesy of Stan Hiller.

Figure 5.25(c): Courtesy of James Baughn at bridgehunter.com

Figures 5.28 and 5.29: © Jason Smith.

Figures 5.30 and 5.66(a): Courtesy of James Baughn at bridgehunter.com

COURSE TEAM ACKNOWLEDGEMENTS

This part was prepared for the course team by Salih Gungor with contributions by Lyndon Edwards, Martin Rist and Michael Fitzpatrick.

T357 COURSE TEAM

Professor Michael Fitzpatrick (course team chair)

Andy Harding (course manager)

Jackie Burnicle (course manager)

ACADEMIC STAFF

Dr Alun Armstrong	Michael Hush
Professor Adrian Demaid	Dr Peter Lewis
Professor Chris Earl	Dr Jim Moffatt
Professor Lyndon Edwards	Dr Ed Murphy
Dr Salih Gungor	Dr Martin Rist

EXTERNAL ASSESSOR

Professor Lindsay Greer, University of Cambridge

CONSULTANT

David Sefton (critical reader)

SUPPORT STAFF

Debbie Derbyshire (course team secretary)

Colin Gagg

Stan Hiller

Pete Ledgard

Rehana Malik

PRODUCTION TEAM

Kirsten Barnett	Chris French
Annette Booz	Carol Houghton
Philippa Broadbent	Jonathan Martyn
Lisa Carrick	Katie Meade
Teresa Cox	Lara Mynors
Sarah Crompton	Deana Plummer
Daphne Cross	Lynn Short
Anna Edgley-Smith	Susanne Umerski
Vicky Eves